THE HISTORY OF
MODERN ISRAEL'S MONEY,

1917 to 1967

Including State Medals and Palestine Mandate

Fully illustrated

By Sylvia Haffner

First Edition

CONTENTS

DEDICATION
To Manny, the Most Tolerant of Husbands
ACKNOWLEDGEMENTS
The author thanks the following contributors
whose help has been sincerely appreciated.
TO THE LATE DR. LEO KADMAN
FOR LAYING THE FOUNDATION

BANK OF ISRAEL, Jerusalem. For their cooperation in supplying mintage figures, photographs, and data on the coins and banknotes of Israel. Governor, Mr. David Horowitz; Head, Currency Supply Unit, Mr. M. Brin.

BANK LEUMI LE-ISRAEL B.M., New York, N.Y. To Mrs. Edith J. Levy, Public Relations, for furnishing background material on Bank Leumi.

CROWN AGENTS FOR OVERSEAS GOVERNMENT, London, England. To Mr. G. E. Brittan for the research and photographs of the Palestine Currency Board Notes.

HERTZ, Van Nuys, California. For supplying coins for photographs and data for coin values.

IMPERIAL METAL INDUSTRY (Kynoch) LTD., Birmingham, England. To Mr. J. Poole, Commercial Manager, for the generous donation of his time in research on mintage figures for the Pruta series.

ISRAEL GOVERNMENT COINS AND MEDALS CORP., Ltd. Jerusalem. To the Director, Yitzhak Avni; Public Relations, Mrs. Myriam Avida; Subscription Dept., Miss Violet Menachem—all of whom served with patience and understanding in supplying photographs, research, and, most of all, encouragement.

DR. ARIE KINDLER, Director of the Kadman Numismatic Museum, Jerusalem. My deepest gratitude for supplying photographs, documents, and research.

THE MINT, BIRMINGHAM, LTD., England. To Mr. D. J. Rodgers for his research and mintage figures for the Pruta series.

ROYAL MINT, London, England. To Mr. G. P. Dyer for his research and mintage figures for the coins of Palestine.

THOMAS DE LA RUE & CO., LTD., London, England. For their research on the banknotes of Palestine and Israel.

NETHERLANDS STATE MINT, Utrecht. To Dr. J.W.A. Van Hengel, Master, for mintage figures on the commemoratives of Israel.

TO THE FOLLOWING NUMISMATISTS WHO SO GENEROUSLY
DONATED THEIR TIME AND KNOWLEDGE:

Henry J. Berube	Menachem Lew-Ran
Jack Brisker	Yaakov Meshorer
Joel Marc Haffner (my son)	Patsy & Harvey Rose
Hershel Herzig	Ury Shalit
Isnumat, Mrs. A. Zemanek	Jonah R. Shapiro

To KEN HEDGES, Editor of INTERCOIN, Spring Valley, Calif., my grammarian and typist unexcelled, who spent many hours readying the manuscript for publication, and photographing the material.

TO ALL UNSUNG HEROES WHO GAVE SO FREELY OF THEIR
KNOWLEDGE AND TIME, THANK YOU AND SHALOM.

All mistakes are mine. Please send all additions and corrections to Sylvia Haffner, P.O. Box 574, La Mesa, Calif. 92041

Hebrew dates before the birth of Christ always carry the symbol BCE (Before the Common Era), and after the birth of Christ CE (Common Era). In order to simplify the dating, this manuscript will include the more common symbols of "BC" and "AD".

HEBREW CHARACTERS OF ALPHABET AND NUMBERS

NO.	LETTER		COMBINATIONS	
1	Aleph	א	·11	י א
2	Beth	ב	12	י ב
3	Gimmel	ג	13	י ג
4	Daleth	ד	14	י ד
5	He	ה	15	ט ו
6	Vav	ו	16	ט ז
7	Zayin	ז	17	י ז
8	Heth	ח	18	י ח
9	Teth	ט	19	י ט
10	Yod	י	21	כ א
20	Chaph	כ	22	כ ב
20	Chaph Sophith	ך		
30	Lamedh	ל		
40	Mem	מ		
50	Nun	נ		
60	Samekh	ס		
70	Ayin	ע		
80	Pe	פ		
90	Sadhe	צ		
100	Koph	ק		
200	Resh	ר		
300	Shin	ש		
400	Tav	ת		

The Hebrew calendar is reckoned from the creation of the universe, which the ancient Hebrews placed at 3760 BC. In the fourth Century AD, Patriarch Hillel II of Tiberias gave the Hebrew calendar its present form. Because the Hebrew New Year occurs either in September or October, it creates an over-lapping of years with the Gregorian calendar. (See chart on inside cover.)

Hebrew numbers are formed from the 22 letters of the Hebrew alphabet, the group of combination letters are shown for the convenience of the reader and represent the way letters are combined to form larger numbers.

There are two characters used for the numeral "20" on the coins of Israel. The first character for "20" on the chart **כ** is used on all of the coins dated from 5721 (1960-1961) through the present date; the second character for the numeral "20" **ך** is used on all coins dated 5720 (1959-1960). Many of the characters have been stylized and differences will be noted between the commemorative series and the trade-coins.

It is customary to eliminate the millenium, (currently "5000") on Israel's coins; the date is thus condensed to the last three numbers. On the paper money of Israel the "5000" is shown. Keeping in mind the year 3760 BC and adding to it the year of 1966, you will arrive at the Hebrew year of 5726.

Hebrew always is read from right to left. In translation the condensed year of 1965-66 (726), you would read from the table as follows:

(From right to left) 6+20+300+400=726=5726=1965-66. Note the stylized "300" **תשכ"ו** used from 1958 (5718) on.

All of the numbers between 11 and 19 are formed by adding 10+1, 10+2, etc., except for the numbers 15 and 16, which are formed by adding 9+6 and 9+7. If the numbers 10+5 and 10+6 were used, the characters would also form a word representing the Deity. Thus the year 1954-55 (715) would read from the table as follows:

(From right to left) 6+9+300+400=715=5715=1954-55 while the

תשט"ו

year 1951-52 (712) would read this way:

(From right to left) 2+10+300+400=712=5712=1951-52

תש"יב

The twenties are formed by adding the character for 20 to the characters for 1, 2, etc. The same procedure is followed for the thirties, forties, and so on.

A pair of characters is found just before the last letter on the left; they resemble quotation marks or apostrophes. Do not confuse these marks with the letter for 10. These marks have no significance in determining the dates; they only serve to accentuate the year, which is always the last letter on the left.

1200-586 BC	**FIRST COMMONWEALTH**
1020-998 BC	**KING SAUL** *There were twelve tribes of Israelites under the monarchy of King David.*
998-965 BC	**KING DAVID**
965-926 BC	**KING SOLOMON** *After the death of Solomon, two kingdoms were created: Israel, the northern kingdom, and Judah, the southern kingdom.*
926-721 BC	**ISRAEL, THE NORTHERN KINGDOM** *Israel fell to the Assyrian Empire in 721 BC. The kingdom was disbanded and the people dispersed through other lands. The Israelites lost their identity through assimilation and are referred to as the "Ten Lost Tribes of Israel."*
926-587 BC	**JUDAH, THE SOUTHERN KINGDOM** *Judah fell to the Babylonians in 587 BC. The city of Jerusalem was destroyed.*
586-70 BC	**SECOND COMMONWEALTH**
587-538 BC	**THE BABYLONIAN CAPTIVITY OF JUDAH**
538-331 BC	**THE PERSIAN CAPTIVITY** *When the Persian King Cyprus captured Babylonia, he permitted the exiled Judeans to return. During this period the rebuilding of Jerusalem and the Temple took place, and the re-establishment of the Hebrews in Judah was accomplished.*
331-301 BC	**THE GREEK CAPTIVITY**
301-198 BC	**THE EGYPTIAN CAPTIVITY**
198-163 BC	**THE SYRIAN CAPTIVITY** *In 168 BC the Syrian King Epiphames robbed the Temple, destroyed all copies of the Scriptures that could be found, and desecrated the Temple by offering heathen sacrifices on its altars. These acts split the Hebrews into two groups and led to the Maccabean Revolt.*
168-129 BC	**THE MACCABEAN REVOLT AND DYNASTY**
129-37 BC	**THE HASMONEAN DYNASTY**
37 BC-AD 44	**THE HERODIAN DYNASTY**
AD 44-66	**THE ROMAN PROCURATORS**
AD 66-70	**FIRST REVOLT: THE WAR OF THE JEWS AGAINST ROME** *Roman Emperor Titus razed the city of Jerusalem and destroyed the Temple in AD 70.*
AD 70-132	**THE ROMAN CAPTIVITY** *During this period many coins were struck to remind the Hebrews of their defeat. These coins are known as the "Judaea Capta" series under Vespasian, Titus and Domitian.*
AD 132-135	**SECOND REVOLT: THE BAR-KOCHBA REVOLT** *The revolt failed disastrously with the slaughter of the followers of Simon, who called himself Messiah, the Son of a Star (Bar-Kochba).*
AD 135-637	**THE ROMAN AND BYZANTINE CAPTIVITY**
AD 637-1099	**THE MOSLEM CAPTIVITY**
AD 1099-1187	**THE CRUSADERS CAPTIVITY**
AD 1187-1517	**THE PERIOD OF NUMEROUS CAPTIVITIES** *Jerusalem changed hands from the Seljuk Turks to the Crusaders, to the Mamelukes of Egypt, and finally to the Ottoman Turks in 1517. During this period various orders, knights and princes retained the title of King of Jerusalem: The Kings of Cyprus, Kings of Sicily, the House of Savoy, the Order of the Hospitallers of St. John, and others are among these.*
AD 1517-1917	**THE OTTOMAN EMPIRE CAPTIVITY** *Jerusalem remained almost constantly under Moslem rule until it was taken by the British in 1917 during World War I.*
AD 1917-1948	**BRITISH PROTECTORATE AND MANDATE**
MAY 15, 1948	**THE STATE OF ISRAEL — THIRD COMMONWEALTH**

ISRAEL

The old-new land of Israel: Old, because here the Patriarchs laid the foundations of the Jewish faith; old, because here David, the Psalmist King, built his city, Jerusalem, and Jesus set up His ministry; old, because here ancient empires and civilizations rose for their brief moment, only to fall again. New, because in our time a nation has been reborn, speaking the revived language of the Old Testament; new, because the land neglected for centuries is now covered with farmlands and fertile fields; new, because the people are new, hailing from seventy lands, all drawn to Israel by the promise and fulfillment of Biblical prophecy.

Israel is only 260 miles long and from 10 to 70 miles wide, but she is also 5000 years DEEP. From under the desert sands, from the ocean floor, and from the secret recesses of remote mountain caves, the treasures of the past are revealed.

Israel is the ancient and the modern. It was the home of the caveman before recorded history. It was ancient Judaea, a colony of Rome and the land occupied by the Crusaders. It is the birthplace of Christ, the cradle of Islam, and the spirit of the Jewish people. It is the metropolitan city of Tel-Aviv. It is atomic power plants, modern hospitals, and a desert made to bloom. Israel is a living symbol of a people's determination to work, sacrifice, and die to preserve their freedom and traditions. To possess the coins of Israel is to own a little of history itself.

In 1917 Britain won Palestine in World War I, and in 1920 the British Mandate over Palestine was established by the League of Nations. The Balfour Declaration of November 2, 1917, designated Palestine as the place for the establishment of a Jewish National Home.

Under the British Mandate, the monetary unit of the Ottoman Empire, the Turkish piastre, circulated until 1924, when it was outlawed by the British. The currency of Egypt issued in 1916-1917 under the British Protectorate was circulated in Palestine until the Palestine Mil was created and introduced in 1927.

The British Mandate over Palestine ended on May 15, 1948. There was much strife for the Jews of Palestine during the twenty-eight years of British rule. The land was one of the most poverty-stricken regions in the Middle East. Ancient forests had been cut down and soil had eroded from the slopes. Sand dunes had piled up along the coasts, blocking the flow of streams to the sea and creating marshes.

Young Jewish pioneers, the Halutzim, drained the swamps and prepared the land for settlement. Colonies were established on a voluntary communal basis. One of the first of these was the Degania settlement on the shores of Lake Kinnereth.

Palestine lacked raw materials for manufacturing, but a flourishing industry grew on the shores of the Dead Sea when the Jews extracted potash, bromine, and salt from the briny waters. The Jordan River was harnessed and power was furnished for many small factories. Industrialization of the ancient land was begun.

ISRAEL

Jewish funds built modern hospitals and educational institutions. The Hebrew Technical Institute in Haifa, and the Hebrew University and Hadassah Rothschild Hospital on Mount Scopus were built. This was greatly due to the efforts of Henrietta Szold, an American and founder of Hadassah, the Women's Zionist Organization of America.

The rapid growth of the Jewish National Home alarmed the Arabs and many religious quarrels and riots followed. In 1939, Britain issued the "white paper" which severely restricted Jewish immigration for five years and banned it altogether after 1944. This white paper revealed plans for a predominantly Arab state which would be closed to Jewish immigration and land purchases, and was in direct opposition to the Balfour Declaration with its promise of a Jewish National Home. Further, the white paper was a breach of the mandate established by the League of Nations.

The United Nations General Assembly, on November 29, 1947, voted to partition Palestine into Jewish and Arab states on May 15, 1948. Parts of old Palestine now belong to Jordan, Lebanon, the United Arab Republic, and the State of Israel.

On May 15, 1948, the State of Israel was born. For the first time in nearly 2000 years, Jews were to live under their own government in the land that was their birthplace. Immigrants began to come — from Egypt, Yemen, Rumania, Algeria. Some walked through burning deserts, some flew in aged planes on the airlift, some came in jam-packed cattle cars, some came in deluxe liners, some came on stretchers, some came blind, some came crippled, and most of them came tortured. From seventy nations the dispersed, the exiles, the unwanted came home to their native land to live without persecution.

From this assortment of human flotsam and jetsam an ancient nation was reborn — a nation whose people possess an endless determination to live in freedom and dignity.

A few hours after the new State of Israel was proclaimed, Arab armies invaded from all sides. The Israelites drove the enemy back until they occupied twice as much territory as the United Nations had proposed for them under partition. An armistice was signed between Israel and the Arab nations in February of 1949, but a peace treaty has never been signed. Surrounded by Arab nations who still threaten to drive her into the sea, Israel must continue to support an out-size army and navy.

As Israel enters her nineteenth year of statehood, she is still a pioneer land and she still faces problems that would give an older, more experienced nation premonitions of utter disaster. The population of Israel in 1948 was about 1,600,000; by 1965 it had swelled to 2,500,000. Considering that Israel's area of 7993 square miles is about that of the state of New Jersey, it was not an easy feat to absorb almost one million people in seventeen years. Israel's Law of the Return guarantees acceptance of every Jew who seeks admission to the new state. Many of the immigrants were physically and mentally ill as well as financially insecure. Most of the immigrants that entered Israel would never have gotten past Ellis Island in New York harbor on the grounds of being too great a risk.

ISRAEL

Most of the immigrants were dependent on the State of Israel for food, shelter, medical care, and rehabilitation. This young state rose to the emergency with unwavering dedication. The sonnet written by Emma Lazarus, in 1884, engraved on a tablet on the Statue of Liberty, could have been written for the State of Israel:

".... Give me your tired, your poor, your
huddled masses yearning to breathe free,
The wretched refuse of your teeming shore,
Send these, the homeless, tempest-tost to me,
I lift my lamp beside the golden door."

The brief history of the State of Israel that you have read here is told in the living symbols of her coins and commemoratives. Civilization has been deeply affected by the artistic influence of the ancient Greeks in the minting of coins throughout the years. The State of Israel has entered the numismatic scene with a true departure from the classical Greek influence. The commemorative coins are suggestive of true medallic art. The artists project through their designs the pioneer spirit, drive, and strength that is Israel today.

BANK LEUMI LE-ISRAEL B.M.
(Anglo-Palestine Bank Limited until 1951)

In 1902, a bank was established under the name of the Anglo-Palestine Company Limited. The bank has operated under Turkish rule, the British Mandate, and now under the State of Israel, and has issued two different forms of currency in the past 64 years.

The establishment of the Anglo-Palestine Company in London in 1902 was due largely to the initiative of Dr. Theodor Herzl. David Leventin opened the first office in the city of Jaffa in 1903, when the country was a neglected district of the old Ottoman Empire, in which civil legislation did not exist, no official land registry existed, and corporate bodies could neither own land nor register mortgages.

The population on both sides of the Jordan River totaled about 500,000, of which the Jews formed an insignificant part. The bank's task was to teach the public about bank loans and how they were to be repaid, and borrowers organized cooperative societies in the villages and towns so that they could receive credit.

In 1914, Turkey entered World War I on the side of Germany. The bank, being English, became an enemy institution. In November, all of the bank's branches were closed by the Turkish authorities and all available cash confiscated. As the bank had foreseen such a possibility, all of the books and most of the cash were not on the premises, enabling the bank to carry on quietly.

The bank's policy throughout the war was to maintain, so far as possible, all Jewish positions and property. It advanced money for the upkeep of citrus groves, saving much property from ruin. To relieve the growing cash shortage and help its depositors, the bank issued the first of its forms of currency: "Registered Cheques" which served as substitute currency until the end of the war.

In 1924, the British Mandate administration took over. These were years of worry, of slow consolidation, and of modest immigration until the beginning of 1932, when a large middle class immigration from Poland set in. This brought about the establishment of factories, especially textile plants. The year 1933 saw the beginning of Jewish persecution in Nazi Germany and of large-scale immigration of German Jews into Palestine. With a view to transferring Jewish capital from Germany, the bank co-operated in the establishment of the Trust and Transfer Office, "Haavara Ltd.," both in Palestine and in Germany. This resulted in saving a good part of the capital of thousands of people who were able to immigrate to Palestine.

BANK LEUMI LE-ISRAEL B.M.

In 1934 the bank was able to help the Jewish colonizing bodies obtain their first foreign loan with Lloyds Bank Ltd. of London in the sum of 500,000 pounds Sterling payable in 15 years.

From 1939 to 1945, during World War II, Jewish industry, agriculture, and building in Palestine were all fully geared to the Allied war effort. Because of increased economic activity and the military spending, some inflation was inevitable, but there also was an accumulation of considerable capital.

The bank was able to finance both military orders given to Palestine's industry and, to some extent, the purchase of new machinery. In 1944, the bank established a long-term industrial credit institution, "Otzar La Tassiya," to re-equip industry and to promote the expansion of the diminutive Tel-Aviv stock exchange, which the bank has fostered since its inception.

In the latter part of 1947 and the early part of 1948, the British Mandate Administration slowly disintegrated, and the problem of the supply of currency became critical. The Palestine Pound, then the country's currency, was gradually being withdrawn. (See the chapter on Banknotes of Israel to see how the bank resolved this emergency and the second form of currency issued by the bank.)

In August of 1948, the provisional government of Israel signed an agreement with the Anglo-Palestine Bank Ltd., by which the bank became the sole banker and financial agent of the State of Israel and issued notes as the country's legal tender. The bank also established a department for the administration of government loans. It continued to exercise all of these functions until new government tools could be shaped.

After the establishment of the State of Israel, it was felt that the bank, as the country's leading commercial banking institution, which was also acting as the bank of issue, should become an Israel company. As a result, Bank Leumi Le-Israel B.M. was incorporated in 1950 and on May 1, 1951, the entire undertaking and all assets and liabilities of the Anglo-Palestine Bank Ltd. were taken over by the new Bank Leumi.

The establishment of the independent State of Israel was followed by several years of heavy immigration, and the bank took steps to help the integration of the new immigrants by bringing its services to them. Branches were opened in newly developing areas, helping them to grow.

Bank Leumi is the largest and oldest bank in Israel and has fostered the upbuilding of the State of Israel. The bank now has branches in Tel-Aviv, Jerusalem, Haifa, and seventy other cities of Israel, as well as branches in New York City, London, Zurich, and representative offices in Frankfurt and Los Angeles.

In 1954 the Bank of Israel was created by law and started functioning as the central bank of issue for Israel. In the course of time the Bank of Israel printed its own notes, removing this function from Bank Leumi.

THE BANK OF ISRAEL

In 1954 the Bank of Israel was created by the Bank of Israel Law and started to operate in December of that year. The law endows the bank with the authority to implement the state's monetary policy:

> "To administer, regulate and direct the currency system and to regulate and direct the credit and banking system in Israel in accordance with the economic policy of the Government, and the provisions of this Law, with view to promoting, by monetary means."

The bank is headed by a governor who, by virtue of the law, also acts as economic adviser to the government. He is counseled by an advisory committee and advisory council. Since the founding of the bank, the governor has been Mr. David Horowitz, now in his third term.

To achieve its statutory objectives, the bank has assumed the duties which are generally associated with central banks:

1. Issuing currency; all notes and coins constituting legal tender in Israel are issued by the bank.

2. Administering monetary and credit policies within the compass of the government's general economic policy.

3. Controlling the banking system, with a view to ensuring compliance with the law and safeguarding the interests of the depositors.

4. Managing Israel's gold and foreign exchange reserves with a view to achieving maximum security and highest possible income.

5. Undertaking open-market operations.

6. Administering clearing arrangements with states Israel has trade and payment agreements.

7. Acting as banker and fiscal agent to the government, administering the government's deposits and borrowings, handling the government's banking business, and administering state loans.

8. Engaging in economic research and publishing some of the results of it in the form of reports to the government, notably the Annual Report, which describes Israel's economic development year by year.

9. Representing the State of Israel in international financial institutions in which it is a member, such as the International Monetary Fund and World Bank.

(Courtesy of the Bank of Israel)

THE ISRAEL GOVERNMENT COINS AND MEDALS CORPORATION LTD.

During the celebrations of the tenth anniversary of the State of Israel in 1958, the Bank of Israel was approached with a suggestion to issue commemorative coins. This new operation was entrusted to a Medals and Coins Section attached to the Prime Minister's office. As the activities of this section expanded and the services of artists, manufacturers, and businessmen were needed, the government established, in 1961, the Israel Coins and Medals Company, Ltd. In late 1963 the company was renamed the Israel Government Coins and Medals Corporation, Ltd. with all of the shares in the corporation owned by the government.

The corporation is headed by a Director General, responsible to a board of directors which represents the Prime Minister's office, the Minister of Finance, Commerce and Industry, the Bank of Israel, and the Government Tourist Corporation.

The corporation is the distributor of the commemorative coins issued by the Bank of Israel and the yearly proof-like sets issued since 1965, as well as the presentation sets issued from 1962 to 1965. It is also the task of the corporation to strike medals in celebration of national and international events, and in honor or in memory of great men and women. The profits from all sales are devoted to the improvement of the landscape and the maintenance and restoration of archaeological sites.

Levi Avrahami was the first Director-General of the corporation serving from 1961 to 1963. Yitzhak Avni is the present Director-General of the corporation. Under the guidance of these two directors, the corporation flourished and the profits from the sale of coins and medals were expended on the preservation and improvement of historical sites, such as:

Caesarea: The Crusader town with its encircling fortified wall was cleared and restored, and the Roman aquaduct and many contemporary buildings, the amphitheatre, and mosaic floors are all now excavated and exposed. New roads give easy access to the several sites.

Acre: Many improvements have been made in this ancient town to bring back some of its former glories. Buildings of the Crusader period were brought to light and their former splendor restored.

The corporation takes pride in having played no small part in bringing about these changes in the preservation and landscaping of historical sites, and its role becomes constantly more important as the number of persons eager to acquire Israel's coins and medals grows.

Although the coins are sold above their nominal face value, and the medals above the intrinsic value of their metallic content, the corporation feels that justification lies in the fact that the coins and medals are issued in strictly limited quantities and the dies are destroyed, insuring no restriking. As a result, the prices of the issues tend to rise as soon as distribution by the corporation has ended.

Any collector of Israel's coins should experience a deep sense of personal satisfaction to be a very real part of the restoration work being done in Israel, so vital for both Christian and Jew alike. He is also the possessor of the world's most beautiful modern coins with their momentous themes and noble artistry.

THE MIL AND PRUTA SERIES

When Israel was reborn on May 15, 1948, the immediate need for currency became apparent. The new government of Israel invited the Israel Numismatic Society to submit designs and proposals for the new coins. Two of the society's members, Leo Kadman and Hannan Pavel; the designer Otte Wallish; and Mr. A. Eylon, Government Printer of Israel, prepared designs for eight coins. In July of 1948, the proposed coin designs were submitted to the Minister of Finance, Eliezer Kaplan, and were approved without alteration by the Inter-Ministerial Commission for Symbols and Designs, and by the government itself.

The designs of the coins were taken from ancient Jewish coins issued 2000 years ago. Of the eight coin designs, three were taken from coins of the War of the Jews Against Rome (AD 66-70); the three pomegranates, the three ears of barley, and the vine leaf. Four designs were taken from the coins of the Bar-Kochba war (AD 132-135): the lyre, the bunch of grapes, the amphora, and the seven-branched palmtree. Two designs were taken from the coins of the Hasmonean Dynasty (129-37 BC): the anchor, and the wreath of olive branches appearing on all the reverses.

The lyre was originally intended for the 250 Pruta and the three ears of barley for the 5 Prutot. Due to a mistake at the mint, the designs were reversed on the two coins, thus creating a disproportion between the size of the coin and the design.

The new coins were intended to revive the ancient Jewish coins and their symbols, and to form a link between the past of the Jewish people and the new State of Israel. They also symbolize the fertility of Israel with the grapes, pomegranates, ears of barley, palmtree, and vine leaf. The anchor represents the navy, the lyre the arts, and the amphora industries.

In 1952 the first change in the designs was made. When the 10 Prutot was changed from copper to aluminum, the amphora was replaced by a jug with a palm branch on either side; this design also was taken from the Bar-Kochba war (AD 132-135). The edge was scalloped to avoid mistaking the 10 Prutot for the 50 Pruta, as the size was similar. In 1957, the 10 Prutot was changed again to a round planchet, for a short time in copper-electroplate-aluminum, and then in aluminum.

In August of 1948, the Finance Ministry decided to mint the new coins of Israel in a local factory in Jerusalem. The 25 Mils was produced of duro aluminum. This issue was not very successful for several reasons: the production was extremely slow and the execution of the artistic and technical factors was very poor, resulting in a great disappointment to the Ministry. It was decided not to release the coins for circulation, but due to the great shortage of small currency they were brought temporarily into use. A very small number of the 25 Mils bears the date 1948/5708/ תש"ח , the only coin of Israel to bear the date 1948. The great majority bear the date 1949/5709/ תש"ט .

According to Hebrew grammar, the digits 2 through 10 inclusive take the plural form of the noun (1 Pruta, but 5 Prutot, 10 Prutot, etc.). But from the number 11 onwards it is more acceptable to use the singular form of the noun (25 Pruta). Two errors have flawed the Israel Pruta coins. The 1949 5 and 10 Prutot and the 1952 10 Prutot all have inscriptions reading "Pruta" instead of "Prutot." In 1957, the 10 Prutot was corrected to read "Prutot."

THE MIL AND PRUTA SERIES

Because of the lack of equipment, the government of Israel farmed out the mintage of her coins to the Metal Division of the Imperial Chemical Industries in Birmingham, England (which was known as the ICI Mint from 1942 to 1962, when it became known as the Imperial Metal Industries; more widely known as the King's Norton Mint or Kynoch Mint). The ICI subcontracted the order, placed by Israel, with the Mint, Birmingham, Ltd. (which though more widely known as Heaton's Mint, shall be referred to in this book as the MBL Mint).

In July of 1949, the 50 and 100 Pruta were placed into circulation, and by the end of 1951, all eight types of the Pruta series had been issued.

Seven of the series, the 1, 5, 10, 25, 50, 100 Pruta and the 250 Pruta of cupronickel, bearing the date 1949, were struck at both mints. The 250 and 500 Pruta in silver, dated 1949, were struck only at the MBL, with the 250 Pruta having the "H" mintmark (for Heaton), the only coin of Israel to bear the Heaton mintmark.

All of the 1949 cupronickel Pruta coins EXCEPT the 100 Pruta occur with a small "pearl" mark under the bar connecting the wreath on the reverse. These coins can be found with pearl **(w/p)** and without pearl **(w/o/p).** This mark has been accredited to the ICI Mint as a mintmark, but the ICI Mint states:

"The pearl was not intended as a mintmark, but was part of the artist's design. The master dies were made by Pinches of London, with the working dies produced both at the ICI and MBL mints. The MBL Mint has stated categorically that none of the coins they minted possessed a pearl mark. The pearl mark came into existence at the ICI Mint after the completion of the 100 Pruta and after part of the 50 Pruta coins were struck. We have no way of knowing which coins were struck at the ICI Mint with dies containing the "pearl mark" as the working dies were destroyed and the master dies sent to Israel.

Therefore, of the mintage figures supplied by the ICI Mint, it would be impossible to state how many of these coins contained the "pearl" and how many did not." (Mr. J. Poole, Commercial Manager, Imperial Metals Industries, Kynoch, Limited.)

The ICI Mint struck proof coins of the 1, 5, 10, 25 and 50 Pruta, and the MBL Mint struck proof coins of the 100 Pruta all dated 1949. These proofs were placed into circulation along with the regular coins and cannot be distinguished readily. They are exceedingly rare in *true* proof condition. No one is sure if they were struck **w/p** or **w/o/p,** EXCEPT for the 100 Pruta struck at the MBL Mint which we know was **w/o/p.**

THE MIL AND PRUTA SERIES

The Pruta series is not dated to the actual year of minting and the 1949 and 1952 coins were struck at the ICI and MBL mints in the following years:

DATE	DENOMINATION	YEAR MINTED		ICI	MBL
1949	1 PRUTA	1950		1,784,000	2,500,000
		1951		876,000	
		1951	PROOF	20,000	
		1953	PROOF	5,000	
1949	5 PRUTOT	1950		632,000	1,566,000
		1951		4,388,000	3,434,000
		1951	PROOF	20,000	
		1953	PROOF	5,000	
1949	10 PRUTOT	1949		1,328,000	1,048,000
		1950		4,848,000	4,952,000
		1950	PROOF	20,000	
		1951		1,180,000	1,500,000
		1952		72,000	
1949	25 PRUTA	1949		1,360,000	1,360,000
		1950		1,140,000	1,140,000
		1950	PROOF	20,000	
		1953		8,000,000	
1949	50 PRUTA	1949		6,020,000	6,000,000
		1950	PROOF	20,000	
1949	100 PRUTA	1949		3,042,000	3,000,000
		1950	PROOF		20,000
1949	250 PRUTA Cupronickel	1950		496,000	524,000
		1952		120,000	
		1953		880,000	
1949	250 PRUTA Silver	1951			18,175
		1952			25,950
1949	500 PRUTA	1951			15,025
		1952			4,825
		1953			13,962
1952	10 PRUTOT Scalloped Alum.	1952		3,250,000	
		1953		4,792,000	
		1954		1,000,000	
		1955		2,000,000	
		1957		3,600,000	
		1958		6,000,000	
		1959		4,800,000	
		1960		600,000	

THE MIL AND PRUTA SERIES

The small issues dated 1949 of the 250 and 500 Pruta in silver, minted at the MBL, were struck to serve numismatic purposes only and were not intended for any special occasion.

In 1954, the Israel government established its own mint in Tel-Aviv and attached it to the Government Printing Office. The presses were purchased in Europe, and four denominations of Pruta were struck. The 10 Prutot was struck in both aluminum and copper-electroplate-aluminum, and dated 1957. The 25, 50, and 100 Pruta were struck in nickel-clad steel and dated 1954. This 100 Pruta was reduced in size from the 1949 issue, and was struck from dies made at the Berne Mint in Switzerland and *one* die made at the Netherlands State Mint in Utrecht. The reduced size 100 Pruta was similar in size to the 50 Pruta and proved unpopular, resulting in its withdrawal after its issue in 1957. Only a very small quantity was placed into circulation and it is estimated that only about 90,000 pieces escaped the melting pot. This issue was replaced by returning the 100 Pruta to its normal size in cupronickel, dated 1955. The Pruta series issued by the Tel-Aviv Mint was struck until 1960.

The Mil and Pruta series consists of 27 coins of nine different denominations, excluding proof issues. Beginning on January 1, 1960, all the coins of the Pruta denominations are being gradually withdrawn from circulation and sold as scrap metal. The conditions of sale provide for the destruction of the coins under supervision of Israeli government representatives, followed by melting. Today very few coins of the Pruta series are left in circulation in Israel, the ten and fifty Pruta were the only denominations circulating in late 1966. According to the Bank of Israel, eighty percent of the total mintage has been withdrawn and destroyed.

All known mintage figures, at this time, are included with a breakdown by mint of issue. All mintage figures as broken down by mint in this chapter are approximate. *The mintage figures cannot be used as a guide to the relative scarcity of a certain issue where the "pearl mark" is concerned,* due to the fact that the number of dies with and without pearl are not available for checking.

The estimated values are shown in "average circulated" and uncirculated conditions only. The uncirculated coins are becoming quite difficult to obtain.

Valuations were compiled from price lists from dealers all over the world, with the relative scarcity kept in mind. As the brilliant uncirculated specimens disappear from the world market, the values shown here will become higher, just as small hoards of uncirculated specimens may be discovered, resulting in prices lower than the values given here. The valuations in this book are furnished purely as a guide, and *are not intended to establish a market value.*

On January 1, 1960, the Israel Government changed the division of the Israeli Pound from 1000 Pruta to the Pound, to 100 Agora, a new denomination, to the Pound. The Agora series will be reviewed in another chapter.

The Tel-Aviv Mint was closed down in October of 1965 after striking the 1966 issue. The new mint in Jerusalem started operations on April 1, 1966.

The official exchange value for the Israeli Pound in mid-1966 was $0.3333.

PRUTA SERIES RARITY TABLE

This table is based on the degree of scarcity in UNCIRCULATED condition only and has been compiled from the present market availability. Their positions may rotate as small hoards are discovered, but during mid-1966 the following coins are rated 1 through 10.

RATING	DATE	DENOMINATION	NUMBER
1.	1948	25 Mils	P-1
2.	1954	100 Pruta Utrecht Die	P-23
3.	1949	50 Pruta W/P	P-15
4.	1954	50 Pruta reeded edge CN	P-17
5.	1949	25 Pruta W/O/P	P-13
6.	1949	25 Mils	P-2
7.	1949	1 Pruta W/O/P	P-4
8.	1949	10 Prutot W/P	P-7
9.	1949	5 Prutot W/O/P	P-6
10.	1949	250 Pruta W/P	P-24

25 MILS
OBVERSE: SYMBOL FROM BAR KOCHBA COIN

The cluster of grapes with leaf and tendril is represented on various silver and bronze coins of the Bar-Kochba War (AD 132-135). The inscription around the grapes read in Hebrew, "SHIMON" (Bar-Kochba). The reverse shows a jug with a palm branch and the legend, "FOR THE FREEDOM OF JERUSALEM." The grapes symbol also is found on the bronze prutot of Herod Archelaus (4 BC to AD 6).

REVERSE: SYMBOL FROM HASMONEAN DYNASTY COIN

The two olive branches, found on the reverses of the coins of the Mil and Pruta series, appear for the first time on the coins of the Hasmonean Dynasty, beginning with those of Yohanan Hyrkanos I (135-104 BC). Between the two olive branches is the inscription in Hebrew, "YOHANAN THE HIGH PRIEST AND THE COMMUNITY OF THE JEWS." On the coins of the other Hasmoneans, according to the case, the name is changed to YEHUDA, YEHONATHAN, or MATTATHIAU.

1948/5708/ תש"ח	Obverse	1949/5709/ תש"ט

OBV: In center, cluster of grapes with tendril and leaf; "ISRAEL" in Hebrew above, in Arabic below.

REV: Between two olive branches, "25 MILS" in Hebrew and Arabic; year of issue 5708 or 5709 in Hebrew.

Metal: aluminum; Edge: plain; Diameter 30mm; Weight 3.3 gm; Rim pearled.

	Date	Mint	M/M	Mintage	Circ.	Unc.
P-1	1948	Jerusalem	none	42,650	$30.00	$200.00
P-2	1949	Jerusalem	none	650,000	7.50	20.00

NOTE: Of this short-lived coin, minted under difficult conditions, only a small quantity was placed in circulation. It has been completely withdrawn and ceased to be legal tender in Israel on June 9, 1950. The dies were cut by the late Mr. Moshe Munro of Jerusalem, and the coins were struck by Alfred Salzman in a mechanical workshop owned by Derech Beit Lechman. Later strikings at Tel-Aviv.

1 PRUTA
SYMBOL FROM THE HASMONEAN COIN

An anchor, the symbol of Jewish rule over the towns on the seaboard and access to the Mediterranean, is taken from a coin of Alexander Jannaeus of the Hasmonean Dynasty (103-76 BC). The Greek inscription "ALEXANDER THE KING" is on the obverse around the anchor. On the reverse appears a star of eight rays, enclosed by a ring. Between the rays is the Hebrew inscription, "JEHONATHAN THE KING." The anchor also appears on the coins of the Herodian Dynasty.

1949/5709/ תש"ט

Enlargement of **"PEARL"**

OBV: An ancient anchor in center; "ISRAEL" in Hebrew above, in Arabic below.

REV: Wreath of stylized olive branches; in center, "1 PRUTA — 5709" in Hebrew. "Pearl" below the link of the wreath.

Metal: aluminum; Edge: plain; Diameter 21mm; Weight 1.3 gm; Rim pearled.

	Date	Mint	Mintage	Pearl	Circ.	Unc.
P-3	1949	ICI	2,660,000			
		MBL	2,500,000			
			5,160,000	w/p	.50	$ 2.00
P-4	1949	Included in above		w/o/p	.50	15.00
P-4a	1949 Proof	ICI	25,000	——	—	———

5 PRUTOT
SYMBOL FROM BAR-KOCHBA COIN

The Lyre was one of the instruments used in the Temple. It characterized, along with other motifs, the yearning to rebuild the Temple, which
was destroyed by Titus in AD 70. The cheli-shaped lyre with four strings
originates on the reverse of a coin of the Bar-Kochba War (AD 132-135),
with the inscription in Hebrew, "YEAR ONE OF THE REDEMPTION OF
ISRAEL." The obverse shows a palm branch with the inscription in Hebrew,
"SIMON PRINCE OF ISRAEL." The legends are in ancient Hebrew script.

1949/5709/ תש"ט

OBV: Ancient lyre with four strings in center; "ISRAEL" in Hebrew
above, in Arabic below.

REV: Wreath of stylized olive branches; in center, "5 PRUTA — 5709" in
Hebrew. "Pearl" below the link of the wreath.

Metal: bronze; Edge: plain; Diameter 20mm; Weight 3.2 gm; Rim
pearled.

	Date	Mint	Mintage	Pearl	Circ.	Unc.
P-5	1949	ICI	5,020,000			
		MBL	5,000,000			
			10,020,000	w/p	.50	$2.00
P-6	1949	Included in above		w/o/p	.50	6.00
P-6a	1949 Proof	ICI	25,000	——	—	——

10 PRUTOT
SYMBOL FROM BAR-KOCHBA COIN

The Amphora with fluted belly and scrolled handles was one in a series of holy vessels depicted on the Bar-Kochba coins (AD 132-135) which expressed the longing for independence and the desire to rebuild the Temple. The inscription in Hebrew on the reverse under the amphora reads "FIRST YEAR OF THE REDEMPTION OF ISRAEL." The obverse shows, within a wreath of leaves the word "JERUSALEM" in Hebrew.

1949/5709/ תש"ט

OBV: Ancient amphora with fluted belly and two scrolled handles in center; "ISRAEL" in Hebrew above, in Arabic below.

REV: Wreath of stylized olive branches; in center, "10 PRUTA — 5709" Hebrew. "Pearl" below the link of the wreath.

Metal: bronze; Edge: plain; Diameter 27mm; Weight 6.1 gm; Rim pearled.

	Date	Mint	Mintage	Pearl	Circ.	Unc.
P-7	1949	ICI	7,428,000			
		MBL	7,500,000			
			14,928,000	w/p	.50	$15.00
P-8	1949	Included in above		w/o/p	.50	2.00
P-8a	1949 Proof	ICI	20,000	——	—	——

10 PRUTOT
SYMBOL FROM BAR-KOCHBA COIN

The Jug with one handle is one of a series of holy vessels seen on the coins of the Bar-Kochba War (AD 132-135), and was used perhaps to contain holy oil for the Temple lamps. The palm branch is a symbol of the palmtree, bearer of one of the seven kinds of fruit mentioned in the Bible, and is a Jewish symbol of the goodness of the land. The inscription around the jug on the reverse reads, in ancient Hebrew script, "ELAZAR THE PRIEST." The obverse shows a wreath of leaves and; in Hebrew, the word "SHMA," an abbreviation of the name Simon.

1952/5712/ תשי"ב

OBV: Ancient jug with one handle, palm branches on both sides; "ISRAEL" in Hebrew above, in Arabic below. Planchet is scalloped.
REV: Wreath of stylized olive branches; in center, "10 PRUTA — 5712" in Hebrew.
Metal: aluminum; Edge: plain; Diameter 24.5mm; Weight 1.6 gm.

	Date	Mint	Mintage	Pearl	Circ.	Unc.
P-9	1952	ICI	26,042,000	none	.25	$1.00

1957/5717/ תשי"ז

	Date	Mint	Mintage	Pearl	Circ.	Unc.
P-10	1957	Tel-Aviv	1,000,000	none	.35	$1.50
	(Same as P-9 except round planchet and value corrected to read "10 PRUTOT.")					
P-11	1957	Tel-Aviv	1,088,000	none	.35	1.50
	(Same as P-10 except struck in copper-electroplate-aluminum.)					

25 PRUTA
SYMBOL FROM BAR-KOCHBA COIN

The cluster of Grapes appears on the coins of the Bar-Kochba War (AD 132-135). A vine worked in gold decorated the entrance to the Holy of Holies in the Temple, which is another mark of its symbolic importance. The cluster of grapes first appeared on the coins of Herod Archelaus of the years 4 BC to AD 6. This Bar-Kochba coin has the inscription "SHIMON" in Hebrew around the grapes. The reverse shows a jug with a palm-branch and the Hebrew inscription, "FOR THE FREEDOM OF JERUSALEM." This same symbol was used on the 25 Mils, but because of that coin's short existence, the design was repeated on the 25 Pruta.

1949/5709/ תש״ט

OBV: In center, cluster of grapes with tendril and vine; "ISRAEL" in Hebrew above, in Arabic below.
REV: Wreath of stylized olive branches; in center, "25 PRUTA — 5709" in Hebrew. "Pearl" below the link of the wreath.
Metal: cupronickel; Edge: milled; Diameter 19.5mm; Weight 2.8 gm; Rim pearled.

	Date	Mint	Mintage	Pearl	Circ.	Unc.
P-12	1949	ICI	10,500,000			
		MBL	2,500,000			
			13,000,000	w/p	.50	$ 2.00
P-13	1949	Included in above		w/o/p	.50	20.00
P-13a	1949 Proof	ICI	20,000	——	—	———

1954/5714/ תשי״ד

OBV: Same as P-12.
REV: Same as P-12 except date, "5714."
Metal: nickel-plated steel; Edge: plain; Diameter 19.5mm; Weight 2.5 gm; Rim pearled.

P-14	1954	Tel-Aviv	3,688,000	none	.50	$ 3.00

NOTE: This issue has been found without the edge plated in uncirculated condition.

50 PRUTA
SYMBOL FROM THE JEWISH-ROMAN WAR

The Vine-Leaf is one of the seven kinds of fruit mentioned in the Bible and is found on coins of the War of the Jews against Rome (AD 66-70). The inscription in Hebrew on the reverse reads "FREEDOM OF ZION." The obverse shows a narrow-necked amphora, with fluted belly, with the inscription in Hebrew, "YEAR TWO." The vine-leaf is also represented on the bronze coins of the Bar-Kochba revolt with the inscription "YEAR THREE."

1949/5709/ תש״ט

OBV: Vine-leaf in center; "ISRAEL" in Hebrew above, in Arabic below.
REV: Wreath of stylized olive branches; in center, "50 PRUTA — 5709" in Hebrew. "Pearl" below the link of the wreath.
Metal: cupronickel; Edge: milled; Diameter 23.5mm; Weight 5.6 gm. Rim pearled.

	Date	Mint	Mintage	Pearl	Circ.	Unc.
P-15	1949	ICI	6,020,000			
		MBL	6,000,000			
			12,020,000	w/p	$25.00	$40.00
P-16	1949	Included in above		w/o/p	.60	5.00
P-16a	1949 Proof	ICI	20,000			

1954/5714/ תשי״ד

P-17	1954	Tel-Aviv	250,000	none	10.00	50.00
	(Same as P-15; coin has milled edge)					
P-18	1954	Tel-Aviv	4,500,000	none	.75	5.00
	(Same as P-17 except plain edge)					
P-19	1954	Tel-Aviv	17,703,337	none	.60	2.00
	(Same as P-18 except struck in nickel-plated steel diameter 23mm, weight 5 gm)					

100 PRUTA
SYMBOL FROM BAR-KOCHBA COIN

   The palm was one of the most frequently used symbols of Israel; even the Romans used it to symbolize the Land of Judah on the Judaea Capta coins. The first palm appeared on the Hebrew coin of Herod Antipas (4 BC-AD 40) and then on the coins of the period of the War of the Jews against Rome (AD 66-70). But on the coins of the Bar-Kochba revolt (AD 132-135) the seven-branched palm tree is the most common symbol. The obverse shows a palmtree and the inscription in Hebrew "SHIMON." The reverse shows a vine-leaf with the legend, "FIRST YEAR OF THE REDEMPTION OF ISRAEL."

1949/5709/ תש"ט	Obverse	1955/5715/ תשט"ו

OBV: In center, seven-branched palmtree with two clusters of dates; "ISRAEL" in Hebrew above, in Arabic below.

REV: Wreath of stylized olive branches; in center, "100 PRUTA — 5709" in Hebrew. **No "pearl,"** since the master dies did not contain the design.

Metal: cupronickel; Edge: milled; Diameter 28.5mm; Weight 11.3 gm; Rim pearled.

	Date	Mint	Mintage	Pearl	Circ.	Unc.
P-20	1949	ICI	3,042,000	none		
		MBL	3,000,000	none		
			6,042,000		.75	$2.00
P-20a	1949 Proof	MBL	20,000	——	——	——
P-21	1955	Tel-Aviv	5,131,071	none	1.00	7.50
	(Same as P-20 except date "5715")					

100 PRUTA
REDUCED SIZE

P-22 Rev.   **P-23 Rev.**

1954/5714/ תשי"ד

OBV: Same as P-20.

REV: Same as P-20 except date "5714."

Metal: nickel-plated steel; Edge: plain; Diameter 25.6mm; Weight 7.25 gm; Rim pearled.

	Date	Mint	Mintage	Pearl	Circ.	Unc.
P-22	1954	Tel-Aviv (Berne die)	700,000	none	$ 1.50	$ 3.00
P-23	1954	Tel-Aviv (Utrecht die)	20,000	none	75.00	125.00

IDENTIFICATION NOTES: **Utrecht die issue, reverse.**

1. The wreath is smaller and further in from the edge.
2. The berries on the wreath are smaller, and closer in, almost touching the wreath at the top.
3. The beading is smaller and rounder and is further in from the edge.
4. The zeroes in "100" are narrower and taller.

NOTE: The 1954 reduced size 100 Pruta was withdrawn from circulation shortly after issue when it was discovered that the similarity in size to the 50 Pruta led to confusion between the two. The number of coins destroyed is not available. The diffrence between the Berne and Utrecht dies was not discovered until 1960, three years after the coins were released in 1957. Of the Berne variety, around 90,000 are believed released and the rest withdrawn. Only about 1000 of the Utrecht die variety are presently believed to exist (not accounting for hoards which might be discovered).

250 PRUTA
SYMBOL FROM THE JEWISH-ROMAN WAR

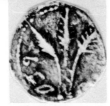

The Three ears of Corn design was derived from the unique silver quarter-shekel, now in the British Museum, struck in the fourth year of the Jewish-Roman war (AD 66-70). In reality, the portrayal is of palm branches, and not ears of corn (corn in the old-world usage, i.e., wheat) as once believed. The inscription on the obverse in Hebrew reads "QUARTER SHEKEL." The reverse shows a wreath of palm branches enclosing the Hebrew letter "DALET" (4). Three ears of corn do appear on the bronze prutot of Agrippa I (AD 42-43). These palm branches have also been listed as ears of barley.

1949/5709   תש"ט

OBV: Three ears of corn joined at the base; "ISRAEL" in Hebrew above, in Arabic below.

REV: Wreath of stylized olive branches; in center, "250 PRUTA—5709" in Hebrew. "Pearl" below the link of the wreath.

Metal: cupronickel; Edge: milled; Diameter 32.2mm; Weight 14.1 gm; Rim: elongated dots.

	Date	Mint	Mintage	Pearl	Circ.	Unc.
P-24	1949	ICI	1,496,000			
		MBL	524,000			
			2,020,000	w/p	$1.75	$5.00
P-25	1949	Included in above		w/o/p	1.50	3.00
P-26	1949-H	MBL	44,125	"H"		6.00

(Same as P-25 except .500 fine silver, weight 14.4 gm, and Heaton mintmark (H) below the link of the wreath.)

500 PRUTA
SYMBOL FROM THE JEWISH-ROMAN WAR

The stem of three Pomegranates is one of the most famous ancient Jewish coin symbols. It appears on the reverse of the shekels and half-shekels struck during the Jewish-Roman War (AD 66-70). Surrounding the pomegranates is the ancient Hebrew inscription, "JERUSALEM THE HOLY." The obverse shows a chalice from the vessels of the Temple, with the Hebrew legend, "SHEKEL OF ISRAEL" and the date of issue. The pomegranate is one of the seven kinds of fruit which symbolized the land's fertility, and is often found in Jewish decorations of the late Second Temple period and afterwards.

1949/5709/ תש"ט

OBV: Branch with three stylized pomegranates in center; "ISRAEL" in Hebrew above, in Arabic below.

REV: Wreath of stylized olive branches; in center, "500 PRUTA—5709" in Hebrew. No pearl occurs on the 500 Pruta.

Metal: .500 fine silver; Edge: milled; Diameter 38mm; Weight 25 gm; Rim: elongated dots.

	Date	Mint	Mintage	Pearl	Circ.	Unc.
P-27	1949	MBL	33,812	none	—	$11.00

THE AGORA AND LIRA (POUND) SERIES

In 1959, when the Israeli government decided to change the division of the Israel Pound into 100 units of a new denomination, several names were considered for the new issue: Gera, Assarion, etc. The Hebrew Academy, Israel's top authority on terminology, decided to call the new issue "Agora," according to I Samuel 2:36, where the phrase "Agorat kessef" (Piece of silver) occurs.

After the new law had been sanctioned by Israel's parliament, the Knesset, the Bank of Israel's Advisory Committee for Coins, Commemorative Coins and Banknotes was instructed to select the designs and symbols for the new coins. The committee decided to retain the same symbols which had been used on the Pruta series because of their popularity, but to stylize the symbols in a modern form. A competition was held among medalists and designers, and the committee selected the designs proposed by Rothschild and Lippmann for the obverses and the designs of the Brothers Shamir for the reverses.

The designs of the coins are taken from the Herodian Dynasty (Agrippa I, AD 43), ears of barley; from the War of the Jews against Rome (AD 66-70), the three pomegranates; from the Bar-Kochba War (AD 132-135), the seven-branched palmtree and the lyre; and from the ancient ruins of the Arch of Titus in Rôme (AD 70), the Menora.

The Agora coins were reduced in size and weight from the corresponding coins in the Pruta series to facilitate their use. The *master dies* for the Agora series were *prepared* by the Swiss Federal Mint at Berne from 1960 to 1966 except for those made at the ICI mint in 1960-1961. The Agora coins, unlike the Pruta series, are dated to the actual year of minting.

The Agora coins have been struck by the following mints:

Tel-Aviv	1960-1966
Berne	1960-1966
ICI	1960-1961
Utrecht	1961

The Tel-Aviv Mint was closed in October of 1965 after striking all 1966 coins. The mint has been transferred to Jerusalem, Israel's capital, where minting operations began on April 1, 1966.

In 1962, the Israel government decided to expand the Agora series with the addition of half-pound and one-pound cupronickel coins. These were issued in the Summer of 1963. It was the intention of the Israel government to have these two new issues replace the half-pound and one-pound banknotes. The Israeli people have been reluctant in accepting the one-pound coin, and in 1964 there were no coins of that denomination struck bearing that date. In 1965 and 1966 a limited number were struck primarily for the proof-like sets. The difference in size between the half-pound and one-pound coins is insufficient for immediate identification, much like the 1954 100 Pruta of reduced size which was rejected for its similarity to the 50 Pruta.

THE AGORA AND LIRA (POUND) SERIES

The 1 Agora of 1963 has been found with a 180-degree rotated reverse (inverted), the first mint error discovered in the Agorot series. Israel's coins normally are in "medal strike" (reverse right side up when obverse is held right side up), whereas the 1 Agora of 1963 error coin is of a "coin strike" (reverse upside down when obverse is held right side up). Most foreign coins are "medal strikes," while United States coins are "coin strikes."

Several varieties have been discovered, most of them resulting from the use of various mints to strike the coins and more than one master die. The author would appreciate any information of varieties as they are discovered, so that they may be incorporated in future editions of the catalog.

The 1960 1 Agora has been discovered with a small and large date. The small date is the normal strike with the large date being quite rare. Some authorities place it in a class with the 1960 1 Agora pattern with eight grains of barley instead of ten grains on the left ear. Actually the large date is the second pattern issued by the ICI, (see chapter on Patterns of Israel). The 1960 1 Agora has been found with a different die used on the obverse. This variety is quite scarce.

The 1961 1, 5, and 10 Agorot also have varieties. The 5 and 10 Agorot show two distinct differences in the two types of dies used, one for the Berne and Tel-Aviv mints, and the other at the ICI. Although the 1 Agora was struck only at the ICI mint, two different dies were evidently used.

The 1962 1, 5 and 10 Agorot and the 1964 10 Agorot are found with large and small dates, the small date being the scarcer variety. Evidently more than one master die was used, although the Bank of Israel mintage figures show that all issues were struck in Tel-Aviv with the master die made at Berne. The large date script is flat and narrow, while the small date script is higher and thicker, there is also a noticeable difference in the fronds of the palmtree. The small date has been found in a ratio of one out of a hundred, and are extremely scarce in uncirculated condition.

The values are given for circulated and uncirculated conditions only. Unlike the Pruta series, the mintage figures here — do serve as a guide to scarcity, *except for the 1960 issue.* This first issue was placed into circulation immediately after the changeover and all are extremely scarce in uncirculated condition, with the 1 Agora of 1960 being exceedingly rare, regardless of the large mintage.

1 AGORA   A-100
SYMBOL FROM THE HERODIAN DYNASTY

Ears of barley first appeared on the bronze prutot of Agrippa I, in the sixth year of his reign (AD43). Barley was one of the seven fruits mentioned in the Bible; it was a symbol of fertility.

OBV: Within an incuse square with rounded corners, three ears of barley; "ISRAEL" in Hebrew below, in Arabic to the left.

REV: Within an incuse square with rounded corners, "1 AGORA" and year of issue in Hebrew. The planchet is scalloped.

Metal: aluminum; Edge: plain; Diameter 20mm, Weight: 1 gm.

	Year	Mint	Mintage	Circ.	Unc.
A-101	1960/5720/(Hebrew)	ICI	12,768,000	.25	$20.00
A-101a	1960/5720/(Hebrew) LD	ICI	Incld. above	RARE	
A-101b	1960/5720/(Hebrew) DD	ICI	Incld. above	$25.00	

Obv. A-101   Rev. A-101   Rev. A-101a L.D.   Obv. A-101b DD

NOTE: A-101a-Reverse; the numeral "I" is thicker and the date is larger, 2nd pattern, (see Pattern Chapter).

A-101b-Obverse; the barley stalks are closer to the word ISRAEL, almost touching; the Hebrew letter LAMEDH—the last letter of ISRAEL reading from right to left—does not have a SERIF on the bottom of the letter.

A-102	1961/5721/(Hebrew)	ICI	19,262,000	.20	5.00
A-102a	1961/5721/(Hebrew)	ICI	Incld. above	1.50	10.00
A-102b	1961/5721/(Hebrew)	ICI	Incld. above	7.50	15.00

Rev. A-102   Rev. A-102a   Rev. A-102b   Obv. A-102b   Obv. A-102

NOTE:
(1st die variety, script is high and and round with small "double apostrophie" between ALEPH and CHAPH.)

(2nd die variety, script is thicker and higher with large "double apostrophe" between ALEPH and CHAPH.)

(3rd die variety, script is flat and narrow with the letters in the date further apart. On the obverse, the leaf on the first "ear of barley" on the left is joined at the bottom of the stem, whereas in varieties "1" and "2" the leaf is joined higher up.)

A-103	1962/5722/ תשכ״ב L-D	Tel-Aviv	3,900,000		
		Berne	10,600,000		
A-103a	1962/5722/ תשכ״ב S-D		14,500,000	.20	.40
			Incld. above	5.00	15.00

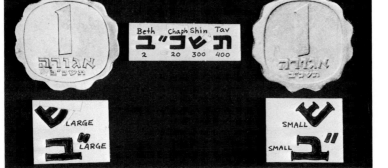

Rev. A-103 L-D   **Rev. A-103a SD**

(The large-date has flat and narrow script with the letters further apart. The small-date has high and round script with the letters in the date close together and a narrow rim. The letters SHIN and BETH have short "upper arms". On the obverse the LEAF is connected in a higher position than on the large date which is connected at the bottom of the stem.)

A-104	1963/5723/ תשכ״ג	Tel-Aviv	8,804,000		
		Berne	6,000,000		
			14,804,000	.20	.40
A-104a	1963/5723/תשכ״ג	Inverted Reverse	Incl. above	1.50	3.00

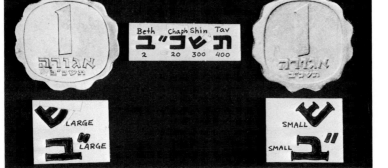

Obv. A-104   Rev. A-104   Obv. A-104a   Rev. A-104a

A-105	1964/5724/ תשכ״ד	Tel-Aviv	22,602,241		
		Berne	4,950,000		
			27,552,241	.15	.25
A-106	1965/5725/ תשכ״ה	Tel-Aviv	10,707,625		
		Berne	10,000,024		
	(150,000 in Proof-like sets)		20,707,649	.15	.30
A-107	1966/5726/ תשכ״ו	Tel-Aviv	8,484,502	.10	.20
		Berne	1,680,000		
	(180,000 in Proof-like sets)		10,164,502		
A-108	1967/5727/ תשכ״ז	Jerusalem	—————	.10	.20
		Berne	—————		
	(155,000 in Proof-like sets)				

NOTE: There is no way to distinguish between Tel-Aviv and Berne mintages.

5 AGOROT   A-200

SYMBOL FROM THE JEWISH-ROMAN WAR

The Pomegranates are found on the Jewish shekels minted during the War of the Jews against Rome (AD 66-70). They are shown in a stylized display of transition between flower and fruit, whereas the modern coin shows the pomegranates in full ripeness.

OBV: Within an incuse square with rounded corners, a branch bearing three pomegranates; "ISRAEL" in Hebrew below, in Arabic to left.

REV: Within an incuse square with rounded corners, "5 AGOROTH" and the year of issue in Hebrew.

Metal: cupronickel-aluminum; Edge: plain; Diameter 17.5mm; Weight 2.3 gm.

	Year	Mint	Mintage	Circ.	Unc.
A-201	1960/5720/ תש״ך	Tel-Aviv	8,019,000	.30	$ 5.00
A-202	1961/5721/ תשכ״א	Tel-Aviv Berne	10,078,000 5,012,000		
			15,090,000	.25	3.00
A-202a	1961/5721/ תשכ״א	ICI	5,000,000	.35	10.00

A-202 (Berne)   **A-202a (ICI)**

NOTE: The script on the Berne die is flat and sharp; the script on the ICI die is high and round with the first two letters of AGOROTH connecting. There is no way to distinguish between Tel-Aviv and Berne mintages.

5 AGOROT   A-200

	Year		Mint	Mintage	Circ.	Unc.
A-203	1962/5722/ תשכ"ב	L-D	Tel-Aviv	11,198,000	.30	.75
A-203a	1962/5722/ תשכ"ב	S-D	Tel-Aviv	included above	$10.00	$25.00

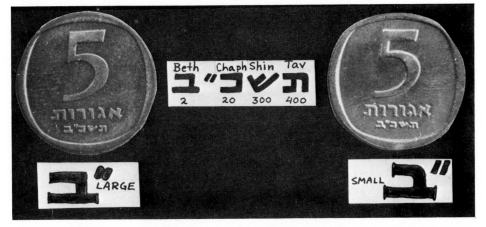

A-203 Large date (L-D)   A-203a Small date (S-D)

NOTE: On the large date variety the script is flat and narrow, and the letters "SHIN" and "BETH" are sharp. On the small date variety the script is higher and thicker, the letters "SHIN" and "BETH" are curved and shorter.

	Year	Mint	Mintage	Circ.	Unc.
A-204	1963/5723/ תשכ"ג	Tel-Aviv	1,429,000	.50	1.25
A-205	1964/5724/ תשכ"ד	Tel-Aviv	21,451	$15.00	$40.00
A-206	1965/5725/ תשכ"ה (150,000 in Proof-like sets)	Tel-Aviv	201,281	.30	.75
A-207	1966/5726/ תשכ"ו (180,000 in Proof-like sets)	Tel-Aviv	290,866	.30	.75
A-208	1967/5727/ תשכ"ז (155,000 in Proof-like sets)	Jerusalem	———	.15	.25

10 AGOROT   A-300
SYMBOL FROM THE BAR-KOCHBA REVOLT

The seven-branched Palmtree was one of the symbols most widely used and occurs on the Bar-Kochba coins (AD 132-135). The obverse shows a palmtree with the Hebrew inscription, "SHIMON." The reverse shows a vine leaf with the Hebrew inscription, "FIRST YEAR OF THE REDEMPTION OF ISRAEL."

OBV: Within an incuse square with rounded corners, a seven-branched palmtree with two clusters of dates; "ISRAEL" in Hebrew below, in Arabic to the left.

REV: Within an incuse square with rounded corners, "10 AGOROTH" and year of issue in Hebrew.

Metal: cupronickel-aluminum; Edge: plain; Diameter 21.5mm; Weight 4.5 gm.

	Year	Mint	Mintage	Circ.	Unc.
A-301	1960/5720/ תש״ך	Tel-Aviv	14,397,000	.50	$5.00
A-302	1961/5721/ תשכ״א	Tel-Aviv	7,726,000		
		Berne	95,000		
			7,821,000	.40	3.50
A-302a	1961/5721/ תשכ״א	ICI	5,000,000	.75	4.50

A-302 (Berne & Tel-Aviv)   A-302a (ICI)

NOTE: The script on the Berne die is flat and sharp; the script on the ICI die is high and round. There is no way to distinguish between the Tel-Aviv and Berne, Mintages, which used the same dies.

	Year		Mint	Mintage	Circ.	Unc.
A-303	1962/5722/ תשכ״ב	L-D	Tel-Aviv	8,845,000	.35	.75
A-303a	1962/5722/ תשכ״ב	S-D	Tel-Aviv	included above	$10.00	$30.00

A-303 LD   A-303a SD

NOTE : On the large date variety the script is flat and narrow, on the small
date variety the script is higher and thicker. The 1962 issue: Large
Date — the letter "SHIN" is sharp with the "quotation marks"
touching the letter "CHAPH", Small Date: the letter "SHIN" is
curved with the quotation marks aloof. The 1964 issue: Large
Date — the letter "SHIN" is curved; Small Date the letter "SHIN"
is sharp.

A-305 LD   A-305a SD

	Year		Mint	Mintage	Circ.	Unc.
A-304	1963/5723/ תשכ״ג		Tel-Aviv	3,931,000	.60	1.00
A-305	1964/5724/ תשכ״ד	L-D	Tel-Aviv	3,612,423	.60	1.00
A-305a	1964/5724/ תשכ״ד	S-D	Tel-Aviv	included above	$15.00	$50.00
A-306	1965/5725/ תשכ״ה (150,000 in Proof-like sets)		Tel-Aviv	200,561	.40	1.00
A-307	1966/5726/ תשכ״ו (180,000 in Proof-like sets)		Tel-Aviv	7,276,610	.40	1.00
A-308	1967/5727/ תשכ״ז (155,000 in Proof-like sets)		Jerusalem	————	.25	.50

25 AGOROT A-400
SYMBOL FROM THE BAR-KOCHBA REVOLT

A similar Lyre (Kithara) with three strings appears on the silver dinars and the bronze coins of the Bar-Kochba Revolt (AD 132-135). The lyre was one of the musical instruments used in the Temple and symbolized the yearning for the restoration of worship in the Temple.

OBV: Within an incuse square with rounded corners, a three-stringed ancient lyre, "ISRAEL" in Hebrew below, in Arabic to the left.

REV: Within an incuse square with rounded corners, "25 AGOROTH" and the date of issue in Hebrew.

Metal: cupronickel-aluminum; Edge: plain; Diameter 25.5mm; Weight 6.5 gm.

	Year	Mint	Mintage	Circ.	Unc.
A-401	1960/5720/ תש"ך	Tel-Aviv	4,351,000		
		Berne	40,000		
			4,391,000	.75	$2.50
A-402	1961/5721/ תשכ"א	Tel-Aviv	2,994,000		
		Berne	2,010,000		
		Utrecht	5,000		
			5,009,000	.60	1.50
A-403	1962/5722/ תשכ"ב	Tel-Aviv	882,000	.75	1.75
A-404	1963/5723/ תשכ"ג	Tel-Aviv	194,000	$1.00	$3.00
	1964/5724/ תשכ"ד	NONE MADE			
A-405	1965/5725/ תשכ"ה	Tel-Aviv	186,544	.75	1.25
	(150,000 in Proof-like sets)				
A-406	1966/5726/ תשכ"ו	Tel-Aviv	320,000	.75	1.25
	(180,000 in Proof-like sets)				
A-407	1967/5727/ תשכ"ז	Jerusalem	———	.50	.75
	(155,000 in Proof-like sets)				

NOTE: There is no way to distinguish between Tel-Aviv, Berne, and Utrecht mintage for the 1960 and 1961 25 Agorot coins.

½ ISRAEL POUND   A-500
SYMBOL FROM THE ARCH OF TITUS

The Menora design on the half-pound coin is a copy of the famous carving on the Arch of Titus in Rome which, on its bas-reliefs, depicts the spoils of the Temple destroyed by the Romans in the year AD 70.

OBV: The emblem of the State, a seven-branched Menora, between two olive branches joined at their bases by the word "ISRAEL" in Hebrew; "ISRAEL" repeated in Arabic on the right, in English on the left.

REV: Numeral "½"; "LIRA ISRAELITH" below; date of issue at bottom in Hebrew.

Metal: .75 copper, .25 nickel; Edge: milled; Diameter 24.5mm; Weight 6.8 gm.

	Year	Mint	Mintage	Circ.	Unc.
A-501	1963/5723/ תשכ"ג	Tel-Aviv Berne	5,593,000 14,000		
			5,607,000	$1.00	$1.75
A-502	1964/5724/ תשכ"ד	Tel-Aviv	3,761,890	.75	1.25
A-503	1965/5725/ תשכ"ה (150,000 in Proof-like sets)	Tel-Aviv	1,551,167	.75	1.50
A-504	1966/5726/ תשכ"ו (180,000 in Proof-like sets)	Tel-Aviv	2,139,000	.75	1.25
A-505	1967/5727/ תשכ"ז (155,000 in Proof-like sets)	Jerusalem	————	.75	1.25

NOTE: There is no way to distinguish between Tel-Aviv and Berne strikes.

1 ISRAEL POUND   A-600

OBV: Same as the half-pound coin, series A-500.

REV: Same as the half-pound coin, series A-500, except with numeral
"1".

Metal: .75 copper, .25 nickel; Edge: milled; Diameter 27.5mm; Weight
9 gm.

	Year	Mint	Mintage	Circ.	Unc.
A-601	1963/5723/ תשכ"ג	Tel-Aviv	4,180,000		
		Berne	32,000		
			4,212,000	$1.00	$2.00
	1964/5724/ תשכ"ד	NONE MADE			
A-602	1965/5725/ תשכ"ה	Tel-Aviv	166,053	1.75	2.50
	(150,000 in Proof-like sets)				
A-603	1966/5726/ תשכ"ו	Tel-Aviv	290,000	1.75	2.50
	(180,000 in Proof-like sets)				
A-604	1967/5727/ תשכ"ז	Jerusalem	———	1.50	2.00
	(155,000 in Proof-like sets)				

NOTE: There is no way to distinguish between Tel-Aviv and Berne mintages.

THE CHANUKA COMMEMORATIVES
AND HALF-SHEKELS

When the Bank of Israel decided to commemorate the 10th anniversary of statehood in 1958, an issue of one-pound coins was proposed, one coin to be struck for each annual Chanuka Festival. A committee nominated by the Prime Minister was entrusted with the task of selecting the designs of the coins and several artists were invited to submit proposals to the committee. The design for the first Chanuka commemorative, a Menora, was submitted by Zvi Narkiss, and is closely related to the design of the first five-pound Independence Day commemorative.

The Chanuka Festival is the "Feast of Lights," which lasts for eight days and usually occurs around Christmas in December. The designs of the Chanuka coins are all symbolic of the history of Israel and persons who figured in that history.

Because the Chanuka coins were all issued in December, following the Jewish New Year in September or October, the dating on the coins may be a little confusing. The dates on the coins are all given in English and in Hebrew, and the Hebrew year always seems one year ahead of the Hebrew date on other Israeli coins of the same year according to the Gregorian calendar. The 1962 Chanuka coin, for example, shows the Hebrew year of 5723, not 5722 as on the Independence Day commemorative (issued on May 15) and other Israeli coins of 1962. This occured because the coins were issued during the period when the two calendar systems overlap. The 1962 coin, for example, was issued after the beginning of the Jewish New Year in September or October, but before the beginning of the Gregorian calendar New Year on January 1. The coin, therefore, is dated 5723, the new Hebrew calendar year, whereas most coins of 1962 are dated 5722. See the dating chart for further clarification.

There are two Chanuka coins dated 1960. The second Chanuka coin (Degania) should have been dated 1959/5720 instead of 1960/5720. The issue was late in getting out, and was evidently an error. Altogether there were six one-pound Chanuka coins struck from 1958 to 1963.

The proof issue of 1958/5719 is not marked with the Hebrew letter "M" (for Meyuchad, meaning "special") and is difficult to ascertain. The rest of the proof issues bear the proof mark.

Proof Mark "M"

With the issue of the regular one-pound coins in 1963, the minting of the one-pound Chanuka commemoratives came to an end. It was feared that two different types of one-pound coins might cause difficulties to persons who were not numismatists.

There were two half-shekel (equivalent to one-half pound) coins issued, one in 1961/5721 and one in 1962/5722; they are identical except for the dates. These were issued in the month of Adar during the Purim Festival. According to Hebrew Law, male Jews over 20 years of age had to pay a yearly half-shekel to the Temple. When the Temple was destroyed in the year AD 70, the shekel dues were abolished, but pious Jews continued to pay half the local unit of currency into a fund for the poor to be distributed at Purim. The half-shekel coin was issued for this traditional contribution and has now been succeeded by the regular issue half-pound coin struck since 1963.

The collection of the half-shekel in the month of Adar is described in the Talmud: Mishna (Shekalim, A:1):

"On the first Adar, they herald the shekalim."

The connection between the half-shekel and Purim is also found in the Talmud: Megilla (pages 13-14), where it is related that Haman was to offer 10,000 shekalim to destroy the people of Israel. As the Jews were collecting shekalim since the first day of Adar, they were well prepared to counter his offer on the fourteenth day of Adar when the episode of Purim occurred.

The values are offered in uncirculated and proof condition only, and are based on the mintage figures and the total availability of each issue. The 1960, one pound of Henrietta Szold, has been purchased by many members of Hadassah as a memento of their founder, thus making this the scarcest of the one pound series for the collector. The 1961 half-shekel is more scarce than the 1962 issue due to the number of pieces that were put away by the Israelis as a replica of the ancient half-shekel.

CHANUKA ONE-POUND COINS
"THE LAW IS LIGHT"

The Menora is the oldest representation of the seven-branched candle-stick. It is taken from a coin of the last Hasmonean ruler, Mattathias Antigonus (40-37 BC), the reverse of which shows the Table of Shew Bread from the Temple.

OBV: Above, "1 ISRAEL POUND" in Hebrew; below, "ISRAEL" in Hebrew and Arabic, date 5719/1958 in Hebrew and English. Designed by Zvi Narkiss.

REV: Above, a Menora between two eight-pointed stars; below, "TORAH OR" (The Torah is Light) in Hebrew. Designed by Zvi Narkiss.

Metal: cupronickel; Edge: plain; Diameter 32mm; Weight 14.2 gm.

	Year	Mint	Mintage	Unc.	Proof
C-1	5719/1958/ תשי״ט	Berne	250,000	$2.50	—
C-1a	5719/1958/ תשי״ט Proof	Berne	5,000	—	—

"JUBILEE OF DEGANIA"

This coin commemorates the 50th anniversary of the foundation of the collective settlement of Degania, "Mother of the Kvuzot," and the jubilee of Israel's collective agricultural movement.

OBV: Above, "ISRAEL" in Hebrew and Arabic; date 5720/1960 in Hebrew and English; below, "1 ISRAEL POUND" in Hebrew. Designed by Miriam Karoli.

REV: View of Degania on Lake Kinnereth with cypresses, palms, and dwellings; "DEGANIA" in Hebrew to the left; "JUBILEE OF COLLECTIVE SETTLEMENT" in Hebrew around the upper rim. Proof mark "M" between the two cypresses. Designed by Rothschild and Lippmann.

Metal: cupronickel; Edge: plain; Diameter 32.5mm; Weight 14:15 gm.

	Year	Mint	Mintage	Unc.	Proof
C-2	5720/1960/ תש״ך	Utrecht	100,000	$3.00	—
C-2a	5720/1960/ תש״ך Proof	Utrecht	5,000	—	$32.50

"CENTENARY OF HENRIETTA SZOLD"

This coin commemorates the centenary of the birth of Henrietta Szold, pioneer of the medical services of Israel, founder of Hadassah, the Women's Zionist Organization of America, and outstanding personality in the Youth Aliya movement.

OBV: An aerial view of Hadassah Medical Center in Jerusalem; above, "ISRAEL" in Hebrew and Arabic; date 5721/1960; below, "1 ISRAEL POUND" in Hebrew. Designed by Rothschild and Lippmann.

REV: The cloaked figure of a shepherdess holding a newborn lamb; above left, "HENRIETTA SZOLD," commemorative dates 5621-5721, and "HADASSAH — YOUTH ALIYA" (Youth Immigration), all in Hebrew. Proof mark "M" on bottom rim. Designed by Jacob Zim.

Metal: cupronickel; Edge: plain; Diameter 32.5mm; Weight 14.2 gm.

	Year		Mint	Mintage	Unc.	Proof
C-3	5721/1960/ תש״כא		Utrecht	17,000	$32.50	
C-3a	5721/1960/ תש״כא	Proof	Utrecht	3,000	—	$132.50

"HEROISM AND SACRIFICE"

This coin commemorates the courage of the Maccabees and their individual acts of heroism. In the battle between the Maccabees and the Seleucides in 162 BC, Elazar Horan gave up his life in solitary combat against the royal elephant. Elazar drove his sword into the underbelly of the elephant which, in falling, crushed him to death, a fate which Elazar knew awaited him.

OBV: In the center, a burning torch; at right "1 ISRAEL POUND" and date 5722/1961; on left rim, "AND HE GAVE UP HIS LIFE IN BATTLE" in Hebrew. Designed by Jacob Zim.

REV: Within an incuse pentagon with unequal sides and rounded corners, a combat elephant bearing Seleucide soldiers; underneath, Elazar Horan stabs the beast. Proof mark "M" on bottom rim. Designed by Gabriel and Maxim Shamir.

Metal: cupronickel; Edge: plain; Diameter 32.2mm; Weight 14.2 gm.

	Year		Mint	Mintage	Unc.	Proof
C-4	5722/1961/ תש״כב		Utrecht	20,000	$7.50	—
C-4a	5722/1961/ תש״כב	Proof	Utrecht	10,000	—	$12.50

"SEVENTEENTH CENTURY CHANUKA LAMP"

This chanuka lamp is from the collection of Bezalel National Museum in Jerusalem; it is an Italian bronze specimen dating from the 17th century. This type of lamp was common in the 15th century in North Africa and Sicily, and by the 18th century had found its way as far north as Poland.

OBV: Within an incuse triangular shape with curved sides, "1 ISRAEL POUND" in Hebrew, "ISRAEL" in Hebrew and Arabic, and the date 5723/1962 below. Designed by Gabriel and Maxim Shamir.

REV: Within an incuse triangular shape with curved sides, a Chanuka lamp seen from the front; "HANUKIA FROM ITALY, 17th CENTURY" in Hebrew below lamp. Proof mark "M" below legend. Designed by Gabriel and Maxim Shamir.

Metal: cupronickel; Edge: plain; Diameter 32.2mm; Weight 14.1 gm.

	Year		Mint	Mintage	Unc.	Proof
C-5	5723/1962/ תשכ"ג		Berne	12,000	$29.50	—
C-5a	5723/1962/ תשכ"ג	Proof	Berne	4,100	—	$37.50

"EIGHTEENTH CENTURY CHANUKA LAMP"

This Chanuka lamp from 18th century North Africa is made of copper and bronze. The elaborate style shows decorative elements of various architectural schools: Roman arches from southern Europe and Sicily, domes and rooftops inspired by Moslem culture, and forms reminiscent of church windows.

OBV: Upon an incuse central panel, "1 ISRAEL POUND" in Hebrew, a decorative design separating the value from "ISRAEL" in Hebrew and Arabic and the date 5724/1963 below. Designed by Gabriel and Maxim Shamir.

REV: Upon an incuse central panel, a Chanuka lamp seen from the front: "HANUKIA FROM NORTH AFRICA, 18th CENTURY" in Hebrew below lamp. Proof mark "M" below legend. Designed by Gabriel and Maxim Shamir.

Metal: cupronickel; Edge: plain; Diameter 32.2mm; Weight 14.1 gm.

	Year		Mint	Mintage	Unc.	Proof
C-6	5724/1963/ תשכ"ד		Utrecht	10,000	$21.50	—
C-6a	5724/1963/ תשכ"ד	Proof	Utrecht	5,500	—	$28.50

HALF-SHEKEL

This coin is designed for actual service as a token payment for the customary Jewish seasonal collection, connected with the Purim Festival in the month of Adar (February-March), of the equivalent of one-half shekel, which every male Jew over 20 years of age had to pay to the Temple before its destruction in AD 70. The custom has not been required but has been traditionally continued since that time. The money in most cases was sent to the Holy Land for the upkeep of learning, thus following the custom that prevailed in the times of the second Jewish commonwealth, when the half-shekel was collected outside the country and sent to Jerusalem as a contribution to the Temple. The present half-shekel makes it possible to tender an Israeli coin of this special denomination.

1961/5721/א"תשכ   Obverse   1962/5722/ב"תשכ

OBV: In center, "HALF ISRAELI POUND" in Hebrew; "ISRAEL" above in Hebrew, at right in Arabic; date at left. Proof mark "M" below center. Designed by Rothschild and Lippmann.

REV: A raised reproduction of an ancient silver half-shekel with beaded rim from the third year of the Jewish-Roman War (AD 66-70), showing in center a chalice, above the chalice two Hebrew letters meaning "YEAR 3," and a surrounding legend reading "HALF A SHEKEL," all in ancient Hebrew script. Designed by Rothschild and Lippmann.

Metal: cupronickel; Edge: plain; Diameter 30mm; Weight 12 gm.

	Year	Mint	Mintage	Unc.	Proof
C-7	5721/1961/א"תשכ	Utrecht	20,000	$21.50	—
C-7a	5721/1961/א"תשכ Proof	Utrecht	5,000	—	$42.50
C-8	5722/1962/ב"תשכ	Utrecht	20,000	9.50	—
C-8a	5722/1962/ב"תשכ Proof	Utrecht	10,000	—	18.50

FIVE POUND INDEPENDENCE DAY ANNIVERSARY COINS

Annually since 1958, the Government of Israel has issued a silver five-pound coin to commemorate the anniversaries of her statehood. In 1957, a special committee was nominated by the Prime Minister to select designs to be used. In 1959, this responsibility was transferred to the Bank of Israel's Advisory Committee for Coins, Commemorative Coins and Banknotes. The first chairman was the late E. H. Hoofien, former General Manager of the Bank Leumi Le-Israel B.M., and the second was Dr. E. Nebenzahl, who is now the State Controller of Israel. Justice A. Wikon of the High Court is the present chairman. The committee is composed of representatives of institutions, public bodies, and organizations such as the Ministry of Culture and Education, the Department of Antiquities, the Archaeological Department of the University, the public museums, the Israel Numismatic Society, the Government Mint, and the Designer's Association. These representatives are purely honorary members of the committee.

The task of the committee is to decide what event or subject is to be commemorated, to set up the conditions of competition among the artists, to choose the most suitable design, and enumerate the details to be executed.

The designs are uniquely modern in their simplicity, with a proud story to relate. They are the world's most beautiful modern series, with an extremely low mintage.

Like the first of the Chanuka coins, the 1958/5718 five-pound issue in proof does not bear the "M" mark (for Meyuchad, meaning "special") to indicate a proof strike. All subsequent proof issues in this series carry the special mark. Until 1964, proof issues came in olive-wood boxes, while the regular issues were encased in plastic holders. The proof mark usually is found on the reverse, except on the 12th, 15th, and 16th anniversary coins, on which it is found on the obverse. The 1958 proof issue is quite difficult to distinguish from regular issue coins.

The 11th anniversary coin, "Ingathering of the Exiles," is the only issue to have a raised inscription on the edge; the rest are all incuse. This is also the only issue that the government of Israel chose to reduce in quantity after striking was completed. One hundred thousand coins were issued in 1959 and 21,000 were melted down in 1962, leaving a balance of 79,000 available to collectors.

TOP: raised
BOTTOM: incuse

According to the Bank of Israel, Jerusalem, ". . . all dies of the commemorative coins have been destroyed; under no conditions will there be restrikes. . . ."

The commemorative coins are issued on May 15 each year, and are distributed by the Bank Leumi Le-Israel and the Israel Government Coins and Medals Corporation Ltd. of Jerusalem.

The growing popularity of the silver five-pound commemoratives is indicated by the increase in prices since the Spring of 1964. The values are offered in uncirculated and proof condition only.

FIVE-POUND INDEPENDENCE DAY COMMEMORATIVES

"MENORA"

The Menora is the immemorial symbol of the Jewish people, often adorning Israel's ancient coins. The coin was issued to celebrate Israel's tenth anniversary in 1958.

OBV: "ISRAEL" in Hebrew and Arabic; date 5718/1958 in Hebrew and English; "5 ISRAEL POUNDS" in Hebrew. Designed by Miriam Karoli.

REV: Within an incuse trapezoid with rounded corners, a stylized seven-branched Menora. No proof mark. Designed by Miriam Karoli.

Metal: .900 fine silver; Edge: incuse inscription, "TENTH ANNIVER-SARY OF THE STATE OF ISRAEL" (inscription faces obverse or reverse); Diameter 34mm; Weight 25 gm.

	Year		Mint	Mintage	Unc.	Proof
C-9	1958/5718/תשי״ח		Utrecht	100,000	$9.00	—
C-9a	1958/5718/תשי״ח	Proof	Utrecht	2,000	—	—

"INGATHERING OF THE EXILES"

The eleven dancers in a circle represent the joy of those who have already entered the land, and their number affirms the eleven years of Israel's independence. The circle is open for those immigrants yet to enter Israel. The coin was issued in 1959 for the eleventh anniversary.

OBV: "ISRAEL" in Hebrew and Arabic; dates 5708-5719 and 1948-1959 in Hebrew and English; "5 ISRAEL POUNDS" in Hebrew. Designed by Miriam Karoli.

REV: Eleven immigrants in a circle left open; in the center of the circle, "THY CHILDREN COME AGAIN TO THEIR OWN BORDER" (Jeremiah 31:17) in Hebrew. Proof mark "M" at the center of the bottom rim. Designed by Rothschild and Lippmann.

Metal: .900 fine silver; Edge: raised inscription in Hebrew, "ELEVENTH YEAR OF THE STATE OF ISRAEL" (inscription faces obverse or reverse); Diameter 34mm; Weight 25 gm.

	Year		Mint	Mintage	Unc.	Proof
C-10	1959/5719/תשי"ט		Berne	79,000	$11.00	—
C-10a	1959/5719/תשי"ט	Proof	Berne	5,000	—	$48.50

"CENTENARY OF THEODOR HERZL"

Theodor Herzl, a Viennese Jew, founded modern political Zionism and gained European fame as a literary journalist and dramatist. He will be remembered for his labors to achieve Israel's return in sovereignty to her own land. Herzl's famous dictum, "If you will it, it is no legend," came true 44 years after his death in 1904. The coin was issued for Israel's 12th anniversary.

OBV: "ISRAEL" in Hebrew and Arabic; dates 5620-5720 and 1860-1960 in Hebrew and English; "5 ISRAEL POUNDS" in Hebrew. Proof mark "M" at bottom rim. Designed by Miriam Karoli.

REV: Above right, a portrait of Herzl within an incuse rectangle with rounded corners; below at rim, the emblem of the State of Israel; at lower left following rim, Hebrew legend, "IT IS NO LEGEND." Designed by Andre Lasserre.

Metal: .900 fine silver; Edge: incuse Hebrew inscription, "TWELFTH YEAR OF THE STATE OF ISRAEL—CENTENARY OF HERZL'S BIRTH" (inscription faces obverse or reverse); Diameter 34mm; Weight 25 gm.

	Year		Mint	Mintage	Unc.	Proof
C-11	1960/5720/ תש"ך		Berne	45,000	$15.00	—
C-11a	1960/5720/ תש"ך	Proof	Berne	5,000	—	$48.50

"BAR-MITZVAH"

"The Bar-Mitzvah" coin was issued to compliment the thirteenth anniversary of Israel. The Bar-Mitzvah is an age-old ceremony which takes place when a boy reaches the age of thirteen, or congregational maturity, and takes his place in the Temple beside his father. The Ark depicted on the coin is a reproduction of an ancient Holy Ark of the third century AD.

OBV: "ISRAEL" in Hebrew and Arabic; 5721/1961 in Hebrew and English; an olive branch with ten leaves and three olives to symbolize thirteen years of independence; "5 ISRAEL POUNDS" in Hebrew. Designed by Zvi Narkiss.

REV: An ancient Ark and Scrolls of the Law, with steps leading up to the Ark; Hebrew inscription "BAR" at right, "MITZVAH" at left. Proof mark "M" at lower right. Designed by Zvi Narkiss.

Metal: .900 fine silver; Edge: incuse Hebrew inscription, "THIRTEENTH YEAR OF THE STATE OF ISRAEL" (inscription faces reverse); Diameter 34mm; Weight 25 gm.

	Year		Mint	Mintage	Unc.	Proof
C-12	1961/5721/ תשכ"א		Utrecht	20,000	$32.50	—
C-12a	1961/5721/ תשכ"א	Proof	Utrecht	5,000	—	$72.50

50

"INDUSTRIALIZATION OF THE NEGEV"

This coin marks the newest and most striking phase of Israel's activities—the establishment of industry in the agriculturally unpromising desert region. The verse from Isaiah, "He shall cause them that come of Jacob to take root: Israel shall blossom and shall bud, and fill the face of the earth with fruit," has been taken to refer to the mineral and industrial wealth that is now being garnered in this otherwise forbidding landscape, the Negev desert region of southern Israel. The coin was issued to mark Israel's fourteenth anniversary.

OBV: At left, "5 ISRAEL POUNDS" in Hebrew; below, "ISRAEL" in Hebrew and Arabic; dates 5722/1962 in Hebrew and English; to the right, a schematic and symbolic design of equipment of the petrochemical industry. Designed by Zvi Narkiss.

REV: A stylized crane against a background of bare hills; below in Hebrew, "ISRAEL SHALL BLOSSOM" (Isaiah 27:6). Proof mark "M" at bottom rim. Designed by Zvi Narkiss.

Metal: .900 fine silver; Edge: incuse inscription in Hebrew, "FOURTEENTH YEAR OF THE STATE OF ISRAEL" (inscription faces the reverse); Diameter 34mm; Weight 25 gm.

	Year		Mint	Mintage	Unc.	Proof
C-13	1962/5722/ תשכ״ב		Utrecht	10,450	$29.50	—
C-13a	1962/5722/ תשכ״ב	Proof	Utrecht	5,050	—	$50.00

"DEVELOPMENT OF ISRAEL'S SEAFARING"

The Hebrews were navigators and mariners during the first and second commonwealths, and symbols of the sea were struck on Jewish coins of that period. This is Israel's most coveted commemorative and one of its finest designs. The coin honors the fifteenth anniversary of Israel's statehood.

OBV: Smokestack of a modern steamer against a background of the Bay of Haifa and Mount Carmel; below, "5 ISRAEL POUNDS" in Hebrew; above right, following curve of rim, "ISRAEL" in Hebrew and Arabic and the dates 5723/1963 in Hebrew and English. Proof mark "M" on bottom rim. Designed by Zvi Narkiss.

REV: An ancient vessel fully rigged and with a bank of oars, modeled after an incised drawing on the wall of a Hasmonean era tomb in Jerusalem; below, in archaic Hebrew script, "YEAR 15 OF THE LIBERATION OF ISRAEL." Designed by Itzhak Behar.

Metal: .900 fine silver; Edge: incuse Hebrew inscription, "FIFTEENTH YEAR OF THE STATE OF ISRAEL" (inscription faces the reverse); Diameter 34mm; Weight 25 gm.

	Year		Mint	Mintage	Unc.	Proof
C-14	1963/5723/תשכ״ג		La Zecca (Rome)	6,000	$165.00	—
C-14a	1963/5723/תשכ״ג	Proof	La Zecca (Rome)	4,500	—	$190.00

"ISRAEL MUSEUM, JERUSALEM"

For years lack of space and appropriate housing had made it impossible to ensure a fitting display of the priceless treasures of Jewish art and archaeological finds. On "Museum Hill" in Jerusalem now stands the Bezalel National Museum, the Biblical and Archaeological Museum, the Shrine of the Book containing the Dead Sea Scrolls, and the Billy Rose Art Garden. This coin honors the opening of the Israel Museum complex and also marks the 16th anniversary of Independence.

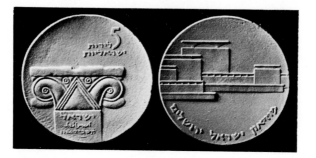

OBV: Replica of a capital from Ramat Rahel (7-8th century BC); above in Hebrew, "5 ISRAEL POUNDS"; below on the pillar, "ISRAEL" in Hebrew and Arabic and the dates 5724/1964 in Hebrew and and English. Proof mark "M" at the bottom of the pillar. Designed by Barak Nachsholi.

REV: A stylized relief design of the museum buildings on "Museum Hill"; Hebrew inscription below, "ISRAEL MUSEUM, JERUSALEM." Designed by Barak Nachsholi.

Metal: .900 fine silver; Edge: incuse Hebrew inscription, "SIXTEENTH YEAR OF THE STATE OF ISRAEL" (inscription faces the obverse); Diameter 34mm; Weight 25 gm.

	Date		Mint	Mintage	Unc.	Proof
C-15	1964/5724/ תשכ"ד		La Zecca (Rome)	11,000	$24.50	—
C-15a	1964/5724/ תשכ"ד	Proof	La Zecca (Rome)	4,500	—	$62.50

"THE KNESSET"

The Knesset is Israel's parliament, the supreme and exclusive legislature of the state. The first session was held on February 14, 1949. The Knesset consists of 120 members elected by proportional representation. Every five years the Knesset elects the president of Israel. The Knesset building in use today was built through the bequest of the late James A. de Rothschild and is located on a lofty hill west of Jerusalem. The coin marks the inauguration of the Knesset building and the seventeenth year of Israel's independence.

OBV: Above left, the emblem of the state, consisting of a seven-branched Menora between two olive branches joined at their bases by the word "ISRAEL" in Hebrew; below this, "ISRAEL" in Arabic and the dates 5725/1965 in Hebrew and English; to the lower right, "5 ISRAEL POUNDS" in Hebrew. Designed by Barak Nachsholi.

REV: A stylized relief of the Knesset building, emphasizing the horizontal lines; below to the right, "KNESSET" in Hebrew. Proof mark "M" at the bottom rim. Designed by Andre Lasserre.

Metal: .900 fine silver; Edge: incuse Hebrew inscription, "SEVENTEENTH YEAR OF THE STATE OF ISRAEL" (inscription faces the obverse); Diameter 34mm; Weight 25 gm.

	Year		Mint	Mintage	Unc.	Proof
C-16	1965/5725/תשכ״ה		La Zecca (Rome)	25,252	$10.00	—
C-16A	1965/5725/תשכ״ה	Proof	La Zecca (Rome)	7,750	—	$15.00

"THE CROWN OF LIFE"

The number eighteen has particular significance for Israel. The letters "YOD" (ten) and "HET" (eight) when reversed spell the word "HAI," meaning "Life." The declaration, "The people of Israel live on" has its origin in the age old cry, "David, King of Israel, lives and endures." This cry was the sign and symbol of hope for renewed statehood. The interplay of HET YOD for YOD HET is a wishful and hopeful reference to life. YOD HET is just a number, but HET YOD has a living connotation. The coin celebrates Israel's eighteenth year of statehood.

OBV: Above left, "ISRAEL" in Hebrew and Arabic with the dates 5726/1966 in Hebrew and English directly below; "5 ISRAEL POUNDS" along lower rim, the numeral 5 greatly enlarged. Proof mark "M" to the right of the numeral 5. Designed by Selig Segal.

REV: A stylized incription over the entire field, in Hebrew, "AM ISRAEL HAI" (The people of Israel live on), the word "HAI" being stressed; at lower left along the rim, the Hebrew inscription, "18 YEARS OF THE STATE OF ISRAEL." Designed by Selig Segal.

Metal: .900 fine silver; Edge: incuse Hebrew inscription, "EIGHTEENTH YEAR OF THE STATE OF ISRAEL" (inscription faces the obverse); Diameter 34mm; Weight 25 gm.

	Year		Mint	Mintage	Unc.	Proof
C-17	1966/5726/תשכ"ו		Utrecht	32,500	$9.00	—
C-17a	1966/5726/תשכ"ו	Proof	Utrecht	10,500	—	$15.00

"THE PORT OF EILAT"

The Red Sea port of Eilat, three thousand years ago had been a bustling port for the convoys of King Solomon's merchantmen. For the next twenty-five centuries, oblivion blanketed the port. Revival came with Israel's War of Independence in 1948, and a banner of the Third Commonwealth fluttered in the Red Sea breezes. At the end of 1956, the Israel Defense Forces in the Sinai Campaign freed Eilat from the stranglehold of the Egyptians and once again, Eilat, is Israel's gateway to and from the East. The coin marks the Tenth Anniversary of the opening of the port to international shipping and the nineteenth year of Israel's independence.

OBV: The entire surface is filled with the numeral "5" in an impressive simplicity; below on the lower half of the "5" "ISRAEL" in Hebrew; below this "ISRAEL" in Arabic and the dates 1967/5727 in English and Hebrew; to the left of the "5" "ISRAEL POUNDS" in Hebrew. Designed by Nathan Karp.

REV: A stylized light-house, illuminating the incription above "A DECADE OF EILAT'S PORT" in Hebrew. Designed by Rothschild and Lippmann. Proof mark "M" at the bottom rim.

Metal: .900 fine silver; Edge: incuse Hebrew inscription, "19th YEAR OF THE STATE OF ISRAEL" (inscription faces the obverse); Diameter 34mm; Weight 25 gm.

	Year		Mint	Mintage	Unc.	Proof
C-18	1967/5727/תשכ"ז		Utrecht	30,000	$8.00	—
C-18a	1967/5727/תשכ"ז	Proof	Utrecht	7,500	—	$12.50

GOLD COINS OF ISRAEL

The Bank of Israel issued its first gold coin in 1960/5720, with a nominal value of 20 Pounds, to commemorate the 100th anniversary of the birth of Theodor Herzl, the founder of modern Zionism. As an Hungarian journalist, Herzl was aroused by the "Dreyfus Affair" and devoted his life to the creation of a Jewish state. The coin is the only Israeli gold piece, at the present time, that can legally be imported into the United States. It was not issued in proof.

In 1962/5723, two gold coins were issued, with the nominal values of 50 and 100 Pounds, to commemorate the tenth anniversary of the death of Chaim Weizmann, the first President of Israel. Dr. Weizmann was born in Russia and became a British citizen in 1910. He was one of the instigators of the "Balfour Declaration" and became the leader of Zionism in 1920. The coins were issued in proof only.

In 1964/5725, a gold coin was issued in the nominal value of 50 Pounds to commemorate the tenth anniversary of the Bank of Israel. It was issued in regular and proof surface. The proof issue of 500 is considered one of Israel's rarest coins, and is very seldom seen for sale.

"CENTENARY OF THEODOR HERZL"

OBV: In the center, the emblem of the state of Israel within a beaded circle broken by the word "ISRAEL" in English at lower left and Arabic at lower right; around the circle, the value "TWENTY ISRAEL POUNDS" above in Hebrew, and the dates 5620-5720/ 1860-1960 in Hebrew and English below. Designed by Miriam Karoli.

REV: At the upper right, a portrait of Herzl within an incuse rectangle with rounded corners; below at the rim, the emblem of the State; at lower left following curve of rim, the Hebrew inscription, "IT IS NO LEGEND." Designed by Andre Lasserre.

Metal: .9166 fine gold; Edge: plain; Diameter 22mm; Weight 7.988 gm.

	Year	Mint	Mintage	Unc.	Proof
G-1	1960/5720/ תש״ך	Berne	10,500	$90.00	—

NOTE: No proof specimens of this coin were struck.

"TENTH ANNIVERSARY OF THE DEATH
OF DR. CHAIM WEIZMANN"

OBV: In the center, the emblem of the State of Israel within a raised circle broken by the word "ISRAEL" in English at lower left and Arabic at lower right; around the circle, the value "FIFTY ISRAEL POUNDS" above in Hebrew, and the dates 5713-5723/1952-1962 in Hebrew and English below. Designed by Miriam Karoli. Proof mark "M" below the emblem of the State.

REV: At the upper right, a portrait of Weizmann within an incuse rectangle with rounded corners; below at the rim, the emblem of the State; at lower left following curve of rim, the Hebrew inscription "CHAIM WEIZMANN." Designed by Andre Lasserre.

Metal: .9166 fine gold; Edge: milled; Diameter 27mm; Weight 13.34 gm.

	Year		Mint	Mintage	Unc.	Proof
G-2	1962/5723/ תשכ"ב	Proof	Berne	6,000	—	$66.50

OBV: Same as G-2 except value, "ONE HUNDRED ISRAEL POUNDS" in Hebrew.

REV: Same as G-2.

Metal: .9166 fine gold; Edge: milled; Diameter 33mm; Weight 26.68 gm.

	Year		Mint	Mintage	Unc.	Proof
G-3	1962/5723/ תשכ"ג	Proof	Berne	6,000	—	$133.50

NOTE: All Chaim Weizmann gold coins were struck in proof.

"TENTH ANNIVERSARY OF THE BANK OF ISRAEL"

OBV: In the center, the emblem of the State of Israel; above in Hebrew, "FIFTY ISRAEL POUNDS"; date 1964 in English to left; date 5725 in Hebrew to right; "ISRAEL" in English and Arabic below. Proof mark "M" below the emblem of the State. Designed by Rothschild and Lippmann.

REV: At upper right, a double cornucopia, between the horns a pomegranate with the grains visible through a split in the rind, in the left horn an ear of barley, in the right horn an olive branch; at lower left, the Hebrew inscription, "TENTH ANNIVERSARY OF THE BANK OF ISRAEL." Designed by Jacob Zim.

Metal: .9166 fine gold; Edge: milled; Diameter 27mm; Weight 13.34 gm.

	Year		Mint	Mintage	Unc.	Proof
G-4	1964/5725/תשכ״ה		Berne	7,000	$85.00	—
G-4a	1964/5725/תשכ״ה	Proof	Berne	500	—	$400.00

NOTE: The double cornucopia first appears in Hebrew art on the currency of the Hasmonean Era, and symbolizes the fertility of the land. To peoples of the Hellenistic culture, the cornucopia was a sign of plenty and usually held an assemblage of fruits and cereals. The Hasmoneans, too, used the form to exemplify a bountiful soil. Some examples of the cornucopia in ancient Hebrew numismatics follow.

1. On a coin of Jochanan Hercanos (67-40 BC) we find a double cornucopia with pomegranate in its center. The pomegranate, one of the seven kinds of fruit with which the land was blessed, lends the motif an original Hebrew flavor.

2. On a coin of Mattathias Antigonus (40-37 BC) we find a double cornucopia with the scattered inscription, "MATTATHIAS THE HIGH PRIEST AND THE COMMUNITY OF THE JEWS," illustrating how the Temple flourished under the High Priesthood.

3. Another coin of Mattathias Antigonus shows a double cornucopia with an ear of wheat between the horns. Wheat (corn) is another of the seven beneficient fruits of the land (along with barley, grapes, figs, pomegranates, olives, and dates).

4. Herod the Great (37-4 BC) also struck coins with the double cornucopia. Here, between the horns, we find, for the first time in Jewish coinage, a design connected with a foreign divinity: a cadeuceus, staff of Hermes, the messenger of the gods.

PATTERNS OF ISRAEL

A few patterns of Israel have come to light in the past few years, and more are sure to turn up in the future.

25 MILS 1948/5708/ תש"ח

The 1948 25 Mils has been found in a uniface strike of the reverse with the obverse blank in duro-aluminum. This piece has been quite controversial as some claim it to be a pattern and others claim it is a misstrike. These coins were struck in a workshop under rather poor conditions and supervision was negligible. It has been stated that 100 pieces were struck without the obverse die thus creating the blank surface. All of the coins were not placed into circulation when the error was discovered and some were taken by a worker in the workshop. In 1958, the widow of the worker sold the pieces to various collectors and dealers in Israel. The quantity that can be traced is about 50 pieces. These uniface coins have been known to be counterfeited by sanding down the obverse to look blank.

1955 COMMEMORATIVES

Upon the opening of the Israel Mint in Tel-Aviv in 1955, the Israel Numismatic Society suggested an issue of commemorative coins to consist of the 25, 50 and 100 Pruta, to commemorate the revival of the Mint after a lapse of 100 years. The designs were to show modern Israel on the obverse and the ancient coins from which the designs were taken on the reverse. The dies were prepared and a set of model pieces were struck when the plan was cancelled for monetary reasons.

Arie Kindler, Director of the Kadman Numismatic Museum, states:

"I have seen these model pieces once, with the late Mr. Kadman, when we received his collection, these pieces were not included. At this time I do not know of their whereabouts."

1 AGORA 1960/5720/תש״ך

In 1960, when the Agorot series was still in the experimental stage, a small number of trial pieces of the 1 Agora was sent by the ICI mint to the Bank of Israel for their approval. The committee appointed to select the designs of the new series disapproved of the left ear of grain containing eight grains the same as the other two ears on the obverse. They requested that ten grains be used on the left ear. On the reverse, they felt that the date was too large and therefore conflicted with the word "agora" just above and requested that the date be reduced.

The seven patterns were then placed into circulation without realizing their numismatic worth. Of the seven patterns released, one is in the Kadman Numismatic Museum, one is in the Israel Government Coins and Medals Corporation's collection, two are in the Bank of Israel, and one is in the hands of a collector who discovered it late in 1966. Of the seven patterns, five are accounted for with two still among the missing.

The large date 1960 1 Agora is evidently an outcropping of the ICI Mint's attempt to satisfy the committee. The obverse contains the "10 grains" as requested, the reverse has a reduced date from the pattern, but . . . evidently it still was not small enough to satisfy the committee and the final design was a *small* date. Just how many of the Large Date 1960 1 Agora were struck no one knows, but it has been estimated somewhere near 100 pieces. This estimate has not been verified.

PRESENTATION SETS (ISRAEL GOVERNMENT ISSUE)

The following presentation sets have been issued by the Israel Government Coins and Medals Corporation Ltd., the distributing agency for overseas collectors.

The first set was specifically prepared by the Government Printer for the Bank of Israel, for presentation purposes only. It is not distributed by the corporation, and is not for sale. As of December, 1965, 200 sets had been prepared: 100 for the Bank of Israel, and 100 for the Government Printer.

| 1965 | **BANK OF ISRAEL PRESENTATION SOUVENIR** |

"SIX DIFFERENT ISSUES OF THE 1963 AGORA SERIES"

Blue, plastic   2.5 x 5.5 inches   200   Not for sale

PRESENTATION SETS (ISRAEL GOVERNMENT ISSUE)

S-1   1962-63   **"SIXTEEN DIFFERENT TRADE COINS OF ISRAEL"**

Pruta: 1, 5, 10 (3), 25, 50, 100 (2), 250 cn, 250, 500 silver.
Agora: 1, 5, 10, 25.

Blue, velvet   6.5 x 9.5 inches   4,000 $26.00

PRESENTATION SETS (ISRAEL GOVERNMENT ISSUE)

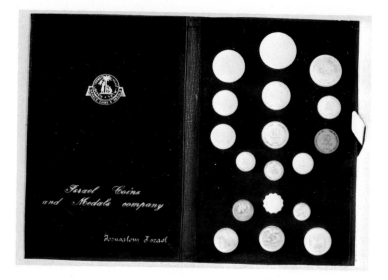

S-2   1963-64   **"EIGHTEEN DIFFERENT TRADE COINS OF ISRAEL"**

Pruta: 1, 5, 10 (3), 25, 50, 100 (2), 250 cn, 250, 500 silver.
Agora: 1, 5, 10, 25 Agora; ½ and 1 pound.

Blue, velvet   6.5 x 9.5 inches   7,000 $25.00

PRESENTATION SETS (ISRAEL GOVERNMENT ISSUE)

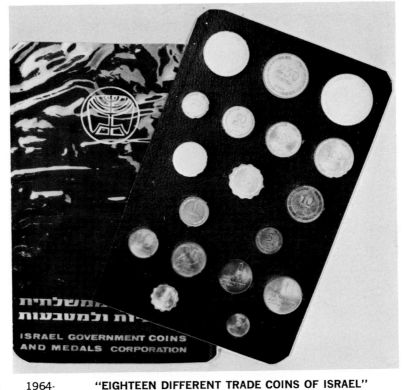

S-3   1964-   **"EIGHTEEN DIFFERENT TRADE COINS OF ISRAEL"**

Pruta: 1, 5, 10 (3), 25, 50, 100 (2), 250 cn, 250, 500 silver.
Agora: 1, 5, 10, 25 Agora; ½ and 1 Pound.

Blue, plastic   6.5 x 9.5 inches   5,000 $21.00
(Not all coins are uncirculated)

PRESENTATION SETS (ISRAEL GOVERNMENT ISSUE)

S-4   1964-   **"SIX DIFFERENT PRUTA DENOMINATIONS"**

Pruta: 1, 10, 25, 50, 100 (2)

Blue/white   4.25 x 6.25 inches   5,000 $4.00
(Coins are not uncirculated)

PRESENTATION SETS (ISRAEL GOVERNMENT ISSUE)

S-5 1964- **"SIX DIFFERENT PRUTA DENOMINATIONS"**

Pruta: 1, 5, 10 (3), 25.

Blue/white 4.25 x 6.25 inches 5,000 $3.00
(Coins are not uncirculated)

PRESENTATION SETS (ISRAEL GOVERNMENT ISSUE)

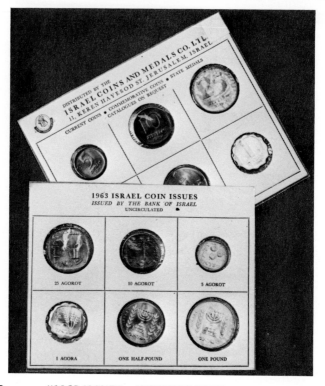

S-6   1963-   **"1963 ISSUES—UNCIRCULATED"**

Agora: 1, 5, 10; ½ and 1 Pound, all 1963; 25 Agorot 1962.

White   4.13 x 5 inches   2,000 $15.00

(This set was issued before the 1963 25 Agorot had been issued; all sets contain a 1962 25 Agorot.)

PRESENTATION SETS (ISRAEL GOVERNMENT ISSUE)

S-7   1963-   **"1963 ISSUES—UNCIRCULATED"**

Agora: 1, 5, 10, 25 Agora; ½ and 1 Pound, all 1963.

Blue/white   4.25 x 6.25 inches   8,000 $7.00

S-7a   1963   **"1963 ISSUES—UNCIRCULATED"**

Same as S-7, except contains the 1 Agora with inverted reverse. An estimate of 1,000 1 Agora with inverted reverse were struck. How many were placed in the sets would be purely conjecture.

PRESENTATION SETS (ISRAEL GOVERNMENT ISSUE)

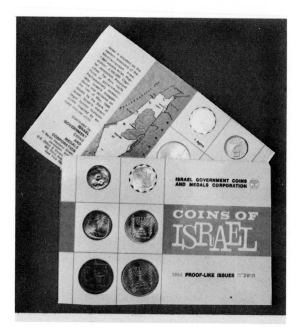

S-8   1965   **"1965 PROOF-LIKE ISSUES"**

Agora: 1, 5, 10, 25 Agora; ½ and 1 Pound, all 1965.

Blue/white   4.25 x 6.5 inches   150,000 $7.00

(This represents practically the entire mintage for 1965; see mintage figures.)

S-9   1966   **"1966 PROOF-LIKE ISSUES"**

Agora: 1, 5, 10, 25 Agora; ½ and 1 Pound, all 1966.

Orange/white   4.25 x 6.5 inches   180,000 $4.00

PRESENTATION SETS (ISRAEL GOVERNMENT ISSUE)

S-10   1966   **"1958-1960 BANKNOTES"**

Five notes ½, 1, 5, 10 and 50 Israel Pounds, crisp unc.
Encased in plastic wallet with numismatic description.

Blue/gold   4 x 8.25 inches   Issue price: $35.00

PRESENTATION SETS (ISRAEL GOVERNMENT ISSUE)

S-11   1967   **"1967 PROOF-LIKE ISSUES"** (Jerusalem Mint)

Agora: 1, 5, 10, 25 Agora; ½ and 1 Pound, all 1967.

Green/white   4.25 x 6 inches   155,000 $4.00

NEW YEAR REMEMBRANCES

Each year, on the occasion of the Jewish New Year, the Israel Government Coins and Medals Corporation Ltd. sends to each of its subscribers a New Year Remembrance. This remembrance is numismatic in character, consisting of some small token given as an expression of good wishes for the coming year.

The custom was begun in 1963, at the beginning of year 5724. The remembrance is intended to serve as a double New Year Remembrance, serving for both the Jewish new year and the Christian new year which follows about two months later.

The New Year Remembrances so far have consisted of an encased one-Agora coin, a numismatic bookmark, and a medalette. Each year's offering takes a new and sometimes unexpected form, and an accumulation of these over several years' time will make an interesting and worthwhile addition to any collection.

The Israel Government Coins and Medals Corporation Ltd. has used two seals or trademarks. The first, Type A, consists of the ISRAEL LIBERATA design from the Medal of Liberation, with "ISRAEL'S COINS & MEDALS" on a ribbon below. The second seal, Type B, simply reproduces the stylized Menora design of the 1958 five-pound commemorative, designed by Miriam Karoli. Both types have been used on New Year Remembrances. Type A was used when the corporation was known as the Israel Coins and Medals Co. Ltd.; Type B has been used since the name of the company was changed to Israel Government Coins and Medals Corporation Ltd. in 1964.

NY-1   5724/1964   Encased coin   Brass   Diameter 33mm

DESCRIPTION: Aluminum One-Agora coin dated 1963 (5723) encased in the center of a brass medalette.

OBV: In center, obverse of one Agora; above, "GOOD YEAR" in Hebrew; below; "5724" in Hebrew.

REV: In center, reverse of one Agora; inscription around, above, "ISRAEL COINS AND MEDALS CO. LTD." in Hebrew; below, the emblem of the company in miniature, Type A.

Edge: Plain.

NEW YEAR REMEMBRANCES

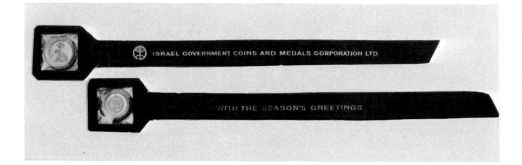

NY-2   5725/1965   Bookmark   Red or black plastic   Length 284mm

DESCRIPTION: Flexible plastic bookmark with a clear plastic window
enclosing a 22mm miniature replica of the second Medal of Liberation (M-21) in bronze. Clear plastic window is to the left when
obverse is facing up. Bookmark occurs in red or black plastic, and
it is possible that a version with Hebrew imprints exists.

OBV: Obverse of miniature medal shows in window to left; along the
length of the bookmark is the emblem of the corporation, Type B,
and "ISRAEL GOVERNMENT COINS AND MEDALS CORPO-
RATION LTD." in English, all imprinted in gold; embossed imprint, "KLEIMAN" may or may not appear at the right end within
a rectangular frame.

REV: Reverse of miniature medal appears in window to left; along length
of bookmark, imprint "WITH THE SEASON'S GREETINGS" in
English in gold; embossed imprint "KLEIMAN" within a rectangular frame appears at the left end. A variety is known without the
gold imprint, "WITH THE SEASON'S GREETINGS."

Edge: The edge of the miniature medal is milled.

NEW YEAR REMEMBRANCES

NY-3   5726/1966   Medalette   White metal   Diameter 30mm

DESCRIPTION: A medalette bearing the design of the 1964 Bank of Israel gold coin (G-4), designed by Jacob Zim.

OBV: In the center, a double cornucopia with an ear of barley in the left horn, an olive branch in the right, and a pomegranate with the grains visible through a split in the rind between the horns; above, "PEACE AND PROSPERITY FOR 5726" in Hebrew; below the same inscription with corresponding date 1966 in English.

REV: At upper left, emblem of the corporation, Type B; at lower left, "ISRAEL/GOVERNMENT/COINS/AND/MEDALS/CORPORA-TION" in English; at upper right, the same inscription in Hebrew.

Edge: Milled.

NEW YEAR REMEMBRANCES

NY-4   5727/1967   Medalette   White metal   Diameter 30mm

DESCRIPTION: A medalette indicating the fruits of Israel.

OBV: On the right, a pair of hands holding pomegranates, a cluster of grapes and a wine goblet; around the rim on the left, "SEASON'S GREETINGS" in English and Hebrew.

REV: In the center, emblem of the corporation, Type B; on the left of the emblem the date 1967 in English, on the right in Hebrew; "ISRAEL GOVERNMENT COINS AND MEDALS CORPORATION," above in Hebrew, below in English.

Edge: Milled.

HAGANAH DEFENSE TOKEN*

Early in 1936, the Arab uprisings against the Jewish settlers in Palestine were increased, with the Arab population outnumbering the Jewish population two to one. The Haganah, (the Jewish Defense Forces) needed financial support in order to defend the Jewish settlers and a small organization of five men was created to raise the necessary funds. The name of the body was "Kofer Hayeshuv" (Redemption of the Country). This committee proposed the raising of the necessary funds by taxation, such as: direct taxes on income and capital; indirect taxes on transportation tickets, theatre tickets, cigarettes and some foods. The Haganah was soon able to operate on the indirect taxes alone.

The Kofer Hayeshuv soon found that there was need for a coin with a value smaller than a mil, (1000 Mils = Palestine Pound) as a one-half mil was collected for each bus ticket and on various foods. The Haganah was placed in control of the design and production of the ½ Mil for security reasons and they were struck in the Plitz factory in Holon in the tens of thousands, selling for face value. The British Mandate Government did not object to the issue of these tokens which circulated until the late Fifties when the new Israeli Government called them in along with the Mandatory coins. They soon disappeared from the market with practically no reserve kept by any of the agencies involved in their creation.

Metal: Brass; Size: 18mm   Circ. $7.50

OBV: The Hebrew legend around the rim, "½ TUV KOFER HAYE-SHUV"; in the center the symbol of the organization.

REV: The incuse impression of the obverse with the shield in higher relief.

*Landau, Dr. Michael, *SYMBOL OF A PEOPLE'S STRUGGLE*, Journal of Israel Numismatics, Vol. 1, No. 2, pp. 33-35, 1966, New Jersey, USA.

EMERGENCY TRANSPORTATION TOKENS

In the early fifties, Israel found itself with a shortage of 5 Prutots in circulation. Several of the co-operative bus companies of Israel issued 3 Mil and 5 Prutot tokens for the purpose of making change. These tokens were issued in small quantities at various times with repeated changes in the series number. The mortality rate of these paper tokens, from the constant handling was extremely high. When the tokens were not redeemed the issuing company then donated the cost of the token to Israel's Red Cross, the "Red Star of David."

DAN BUS COMPANY   **ESHED BUS COMPANY**

Size: 1¼″ x 1⅝″; Color: White, black lettering and insignia.

OBV: In the center, the insignia of each bus company surrounded by a red star of David; above and beneath the star in English and Hebrew, "5 PRUTOT"; below in Hebrew, "FARE GOOD FOR TRAVEL BY DAN (ESHED) SERVICES."

REV: Above in Hebrew, "THIS IS NOT GOOD FOR TRAVEL EXCEPT ON THIS TRANSIT LINE"; followed by, "TEL-AVIV" (Dan), "HAIFA" (Eshed); below in English and Hebrew the serial numbers with each series having a number common to each issue.

IHUD-REGEV. LTD. BUS COMPANY

Size: 1¼″ x 1½″; Color: White, white and red lettering

OBV: In the center, a large red circle with the numeral "3" on four corners; within the circle above in Hebrew, "IHUD-REGEV, LTD."; below in Hebrew, "QIRYAT YAM/GOOD FOR ONE FARE," below the numeral "3" and "MILS" in English on the right and Hebrew on the left; below in English, "FARE"; around the bottom of the circle, "IHUD-REGEV, LTD."

REV: In English and Hebrew the series numbers in red.

ISRAEL-CANADA FRIENDSHIP TOKEN

In 1967, the Israel Government Coins and Medals Corp. Ltd., issued a token to commemorate and honor Canada's Centennial of Confederation. The Friendship Token was conceived to symbolize the peaceful and friendly relations which exist between Israel and Canada. The Token was distributed at the Israel Pavilion at "EXPO 67" in Montreal, Canada, following official presentations to Canadian government leaders of specimens struck in gold. The token was designed by Oscar Harris, of New York, former Chief Engraver of the U.S. Mint, and struck by the Franklin Mint of Yeadon, Pennsylvania, U.S.A.

Metal: Nickel alloy; Size: 38.8mm.

OBV: A stylized maple leaf, superimposed on a graphic rendering of the Star of David; the legend, "ISRAEL SALUTES CANADA'S INDEPENDENCE 1867-1967," in English and French around the rim; below the Star of David in Hebrew and English, "STATE OF ISRAEL" together with the Candelabra emblem of the State of Israel.

REV: A stylized map of Canada in outline; below the quotation from the bible, ". . . AND PEACE WITHOUT END, ISAIAH 9:6" in English, French and Hebrew.

THE BANKNOTES OF ISRAEL

Israel became a state on May 15, 1948, but it was not until August 17, 1948, that the Israel Law for banknotes became effective. Until May 15, 1948, the British Currency Board notes, issued under the British mandatory rule in Palestine (1927-1948), were the notes in circulation. These notes were always convertible into British Sterling. In February of 1948, Britain dropped Palestine from the Sterling bloc, Palestine currency became foreign currency, and Palestine Sterling holdings in London were blocked.

The last member of the Palestine Currency Board left Israel on May 15, 1948, without having made any provisional arrangement. This meant that the currency ceased to function.

The day the State of Israel was proclaimed, surrounding Arab states invaded from all sides. One of the many dangers facing Israel at this time was monetary chaos, which never materialized because, in anticipation of any situation, the Provisional Government of Israel had taken a number of precautionary steps.

First, the Anglo-Palestine Bank Ltd. (Bank of Leumi after 1951) had converted several million pounds Sterling into Palestine Currency Board Notes and stored them away in vaults.

Second, at the beginning of 1948, the late E. L. Hoofien, who was General Manager of the Anglo-Palestine Bank, had gone to the United States to place an order for new banknotes for the proposed State of Israel.

Third, the Anglo-Palestine Bank printed cheques to be issued if the new banknotes did not arrive on time.

Mr. Hoofien ran into several difficulties in obtaining new notes for Israel. First, printing companies were not prepared to accept an order for delivery sooner than 18 months after the order was placed. Second, the printing of banknotes for Palestine at the time of the British Mandate was illegal. Third, the companies had only printed banknotes for governments of sovereign states, which Israel was not at the time. Fourth, the name of the monetary unit as well as the name of the future Jewish issuing authority was unknown.

The American Banknote Company finally consented to print the banknotes with delivery promised in three to four months. Because of the limited time, the company used a combination of existing "guilloches," and since watermarks could not be prepared in time, tiny particles of metal were added to the paper for security reasons.

As the name of the future central bank was not yet known, nor the future denomination for the notes, the notes were printed in the name of the Anglo-Palestine Bank Ltd. and in units of the Palestine Pound. The American Banknote Company would not allow use of its name on the banknotes because it felt that the notes were not up to its usual standards.

The notes did not contain a legal tender clause because of the absence of a legal parliament. Instead, the legend, "THE BANK WILL ACCEPT THIS NOTE FOR PAYMENT IN ANY ACCOUNT" was printed by the company. After the notes were delivered to Israel, they were overprinted with the legend, "LEGAL TENDER FOR PAYMENT OF ANY AMOUNT."

At the same time that the new notes were being printed in the United States, the Anglo-Palestine Bank printed cheques in Tel-Aviv in denominations of 500 Mils and 1, 5, 10, and 50 Palestine Pounds as an emergency measure in the event the new banknotes did not arrive on time. The cheques were the same sizes and colors as the regular Palestine banknotes, and were printed at a secret location guarded by the Haganah (the Jewish underground forces). These cheques were dated May 15, 1948. Never placed into circulation, they were destroyed in October of 1948. One set was presented by the Anglo-Palestine Bank to the Numismatic Museum of Tel-Aviv (now known as the Kadman Numismatic Museum).

When the banknotes were ready in America, the serious problem arose of how to transport them to Israel. The Lod airport was not in the hands of Israeli forces at the time, and every plane was needed for the war with the Arabs. Besides, there were no transport planes in Israel! Only K.L.M. Airlines (Royal Dutch Airlines) was prepared to help the new nation, and two Skymasters were chartered to bring the new banknotes to the emergency airfield at Ein-Shemer. The notes were then transferred by armored car first to Haifa, and later to Tel-Aviv. By the end of July, 1948, they were in the vaults of the Anglo-Palestine Bank.

On August 17, 1948, the Knesset (parliament of Israel) created the Bank Notes Ordinance, which contained a charter between the government of Israel and the Anglo-Palestine Bank.

With this agreement, the new notes became legal currency of the State of Israel. This charter authorized the bank to issue notes of 500 Mils and over, with the issue of coins and fractional notes up to 500 Mils remaining in the hands of the Treasury.

The notes issued by the Anglo-Palestine Bank were covered by special reserve funds which were adjusted according to the development of the currency.

On August 18, 1948, the new notes were issued. No one took notice of the fact that the monetary unit of Israel was the "Israel Pound" whereas the denomination "Palestine Pound" was printed on the new banknotes. In the period between May 15 and August 18, the population of Israel showed unprecedented discipline: there were no runs on the banks and the five million pounds in Palestine Currency Board Notes remained stored untouched.

These stored notes were now to be sent to London and exchanged for Sterling to be used as backing for the new banknotes of Israel. According to English law, the Bank of England was obliged to accept any note at least half of which was delivered. The Anglo-Palestine Bank cut the Palestine Currency Board Notes in half. When receipt of the first halves was acknowledged from London, the second halves were sent. This eliminated the risk in transferring the notes and there was no need for insurance. The cutting of the notes accounts for some of the difficulty in obtaining specimens of the Palestine Currency Board Notes.

The first issue of Israel's banknotes was withdrawn in June of 1952 and is no longer legal tender in Israel. These notes were designed by E. L. Hoofien, General Manager of the Anglo-Palestine Bank, with the help of the American Banknote Company. The front-side inscriptions are in Hebrew, while those on the back are in English and Arabic.

The Treasury of the government of Israel issued fractional currency of 50 and 100 Mils from October of 1948 to 1950, when they were withdrawn from circulation. These notes are extremely rare and counterfeits are known to exist.

When the State of Israel settled down after the invasion of the Arabs, it was decided that the bank of issue should become an Israel company. In 1950 Bank Leumi Le-Israel was incorporated, and on May 1, 1951, the Anglo-Palestine Bank became the Bank Leumi (which means "National" in Hebrew). The Israel Pound was established and divided into 1000 Pruta. The second issue of Israel's banknotes was also printed by the American Banknote Company, in June of 1952. They were almost a reprint of the first issue except for size and color and the fact that they carried the name of the Bank Leumi and omitted the makeshift payment legend. These notes were issued in denominations of 500 Pruta, 1, 5, 10, and 50 Israel Pounds. The Treasury of the government of Israel issued its second and third series of fractional currency in denominations of 50 and 100 Pruta in 1952 and 250 Pruta in 1953. These notes have gradually been withdrawn since 1954.

The Bank of Israel was established in 1954. The third issue of Israel's banknotes was issued in August of 1955, bearing the name of the Bank of Israel. The designs were radical and were not favorably received. The notes were issued in denominations of 500 Pruta, 1, 5, 10, and 50 Israel Pounds, and were withdrawn from circulation in 1958. These notes were printed by Thomas de la Rue & Co. of London.

After the failure of the 1955 issue from the standpoint of public acceptance of the designs, the Bank of Israel decided on a new series of designs for the notes. The front of each note was to be devoted to modern Israel by featuring one of the main industries of the new State, while the back of the note would be devoted to ancient Israel with an archaeological object as its theme. The fourth issue was placed into circulation in the denominations of ½, 1, 5, and 10 Israel Pounds in 1958 and a 50-Pound note was issued in 1960. The notes were printed by Enschede of the Netherlands and Thomas de la Rue & Co. of London.

The fifth issue of Israel's banknotes will not include the ½ and 1 Pound denominations as they are gradually being replaced by the ½ and 1 Pound coins. The proposed issue will consist of the 5, 10, 50 and 100 Israel Pounds and will be characterized by the portraits of outstanding Jewish personalities, such as Theodor Herzl, Chaim Weizmann, Chaim Nachman Bialik, and Professor Albert Einstein.

The first three issues of Israel's banknotes and all the fractional currency are exceedingly difficult to obtain. A choice crisp note will bring any price the seller may demand. The 50 Pound notes are almost impossible to obtain in any condition. Counterfeit notes are known to exist. The fourth issue is available and can still be purchased from the Israel Government Coins and Medals Corp. Ltd. at a little above face value ($0.3333 per Israel Pound).

FIRST ISSUE FRACTIONAL NOTES — 1948

Issued by :	The Treasury, Government of Israel.
Issued :	October, 1948.
Withdrawn :	1950, completely withdrawn and destroyed (still legal tender and redeemable at face value by the Bank of Israel).
Printed by :	E. Levin-Epstein Press Ltd. in Israel by the Government's Printer.
Denomination :	Palestine Mils (1000 Mils = 1 Palestine Pound).
Date :	None.
Watermark :	None.
Designer :	Otte Wallish
Serial Nos :	On face of note.

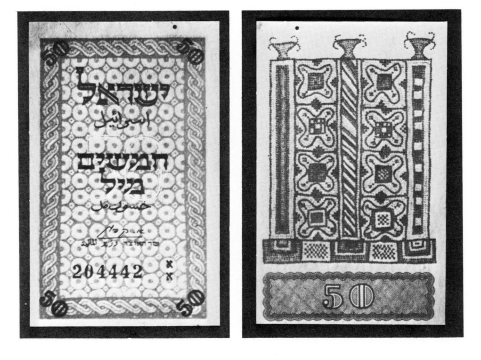

N-1   **50 MILS**   **Size: 48 x 80mm**   **Color: light red**   **500,000 issued**

FACE :   Background, the design of an ancient synagogue mosaic pavement; at top, "ISRAEL" in Hebrew and Arabic; in center, "FIFTY MILS" in Hebrew and Arabic; at bottom, signature of A. Kaplan and "MINISTER OF FINANCE" in Arabic and Hebrew; in each corner, the numeral "50" set at an angle. Serial number in black below signature.

BACK :   The design of a Tora shrine in Mosaic from the floor of the ancient synagogue at Beth Alfah (6th century AD); below, the numeral "50" within a decorative frame.   Crisp $45.00

N-2   **100 MILS**   **Size: 48 x 80mm**   **Color: light green**   **1,643,000 issued**

FACE: Same as N-1 except change in denomination to "ONE HUNDRED MILS" and change in numerals at corners to "100." Serial number in red below the signature.

BACK: Same as N-1 except numeral "100."   Crisp $45.00

SECOND ISSUE FRACTIONAL NOTES — 1952

Issued by :	The Treasury, Government of Israel.
Issued :	February-March, 1952.
Withdrawn :	1954, nearly wholly withdrawn and destroyed (still legal tender and redeemable at face value by the Bank of Israel).
Printed by :	The Israel Government's Printing Press, Jerusalem.
Denomination :	Pruta (1000 Pruta = 1 Israel Pound).
Date :	None.
Watermark :	None, metal security planchets in paper on some issues.
Designer :	I. David
Serial Nos :	On back of note.

N-3A   N-3 BACK

N-3C   N-3D

N-3   50 PRUTA   Size: 70 x 42mm   Color: see note   33,239,000 issued

FACE: Background, an ornamental design with the numeral "50" in the center; at top, "STATE OF ISRAEL" in Hebrew and Arabic; to left, "PRUTA" in Hebrew above and Arabic below the numeral "50"; to right, "LEGAL TENDER" in Hebrew; at lower left, signature and "COMPTROLLER GENERAL" in Hebrew; at lower right, signature and "MINISTER OF FINANCE" in Hebrew; all within an ornamental frame.

BACK: In center, within an ornamental design in shades of red, the numeral "50". Serial numbers on both sides in green, number on right has series letter (A, B, C) in Hebrew, number on left is a different number and has no series letter.

NOTE: Signatures and color combinations known so far include the following.

A. M. Zagaggi—E. Kaplan   Color: Blue   Crisp $20.00
  (Center design on back in black)
B. M. Zagaggi—E. Kaplan   Color: Orange   Crisp   20.00
C. M. Zagaggi—L. Eshkol   Color: Orange   Crisp   10.00
D. A. Neeman—L. Eshkol   Color: Orange   Crisp   2.00

All combinations of signatures and colors are not recorded at this time. Differences in paper are also noted. The author would appreciate information on other combinations as they are discovered.

N-4A   **N-4 BACK**

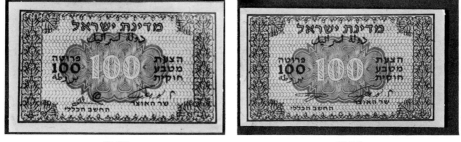

N-4B   **N-4C**

N-4   100 PRUTA   Size: 70 x 42mm   Color: see note   40,481,000 issued

FACE: Same as N-3 except for denomination change to 100.

BACK: Same as N-3 except for denomination change to 100; center design in green.

NOTE: Signatures and color combinations known so far include the following:

A. M. Zagaggi—W. Kaplan   Color: Green   Crisp $20.00
(Center design on back in black.)

B. M. Zagaggi—L. Eshkol   Color: Blue   Crisp   10.00

C. A. Neeman—L. Eshkol   Color: Blue   Crisp   2.00

D. A. Neeman—L. Eshkol   Color: Blue   _____

(Signature of A. Neeman upside-down on series 0101-0120C.)
Note under N-3 applies here also.

THIRD ISSUE OF FRACTIONAL NOTES —

Issued by :	The Treasury, Government of Israel.
Issued :	November, 1953.
Withdrawn :	Being withdrawn; still legal tender and redeemable at face value by the Bank of Israel.
Printed by :	The Israel Government's Printing Press, Jerusalem.
Denomination :	Pruta.
Date :	None.
Watermark :	None, metal security planchets in paper on some issues.
Designer :	Shamir Brothers
Serial Nos :	In black on face of note.

N-5   250 PRUTA   Size: 100 x 55mm   Color: green   12,582,500 issued

FACE: At top, "STATE OF ISRAEL" to left in Arabic, to right in Hebrew; in center within an ornamental design, "TWO HUNDRED FIFTY/PRUTA" in Hebrew; to right and to left, printed vertically, "LEGAL TENDER" in Hebrew; at lower left, signature "A. Neeman" and "COMPTROLLER GENERAL" in Hebrew; at lower right, signature "L. Eshkol" and "MINISTER OF FINANCE" in Hebrew; numeral "250" set at an angle in upper left and lower right corners in English, in upper right and lower left corners in Arabic. Serial numbers in black at upper left and upper right; number at upper right is different number than at upper left and has serial letter in Hebrew.

BACK: At left, numeral "250" within ornamental design; at right, a framed picture of Lake Genezaret with Mount Arbel in background and plantations of the collective settlement Kibbutz Ginessar on the shore.

NOTE: Notes occur in varying shades of green; beige, brown, and gold also figure in the color scheme, especially in the frame of the picture on the reverse.   Crisp $1.50

FIRST ISSUE BANKNOTES, ANGLO-PALESTINE BANK LTD.—1948

Issued by :	Anglo-Palestine Bank Ltd.
Issued :	August, 1948.
Withdrawn :	June, 1953; withdrawn completely, no longer legal tender.
Printed by :	American Bankenote Company.
Denomination :	Palestine Pound (= 1000 Mils).
Date :	None.
Watermark :	None, metal security planchets in paper.
Designer :	E. L. Hoofien.
Serial Nos :	In red or black on face of the note.

N-6   500 MILS   Size: 148 x 72mm   Color: grey on pinkish background

FACE: In Hebrew above, "THE ANGLO-PALESTINE BANK LIMITED/
WILL PAY TO THE BEARER/500 MILS/THE BANK WILL
ACCEPT THIS NOTE FOR PAYMENT IN ANY ACCOUNT,"
the denomination appearing within an ornamental design in center
which divides the last line. In English below, "THE ANGLO-
PALESTINE BANK LIMITED/WILL PAY TO THE BEARER/
FIVE HUNDRED MILS/TEL-AVIV" with "S. HOOFIEN" to
left and "A. BARTH" to right at the bottom. Signature of S.
Hoofien to right of center design, and signature of A. Barth to
left of center design; "TEL-AVIV" in Hebrew above signature of
S. Hoofien. Numeral "500" in each corner, horizontally at top and
at an angle at bottom; legend within frame at bottom of ornamental border, "THE BANK WILL ACCEPT THIS NOTE FOR
PAYMENT IN ANY ACCOUNT" in English. Serial numbers in
red at upper left and right. Overprint, "LEGAL TENDER FOR
PAYMENT OF ANY AMOUNT" in Hebrew to left and English
to right on same line as "WILL PAY TO THE BEARER" in
English.

BACK: Same as the face of the note except that all numerals and Hebrew
legends, including the signatures of S. Hoofien and A. Barth, are
replaced by Arabic; and the overprint "LEGAL TENDER FOR
PAYMENT OF ANY AMOUNT" is in Arabic to left and English
to right just below the signatures. Ornamental designs differ, and
there are no serial numbers on the back.   Circ. $6.00
                                                  Crisp $25.00

N-7   **ONE PALESTINE POUND**   Size: 150 x 75mm   Color: light blue on greenish background.

FACE: Same as N-6 except change in denomination to "ONE PALES-TINE POUND" and overprint, "LEGAL TENDER FOR PAYMENT OF ANY AMOUNT" is printed vertically in Hebrew at the far left and in English at the far right. Numerals at the lower corners are not set at an angle, and serial numbers appear in red.

BACK: Same as N-6 except for change in denomination; Arabic numerals "1" in corners are set at an angle.   Circ. $5.00
Crisp $10.00

N-8   FIVE PALESTINE POUNDS   Size: 150 x 78mm   Color: brown on tan background.

FACE: Same as N-7 except for change in denomination; numerals "5" in corners are set at an angle; serial numbers appear in black.

BACK: Same as N-6 except for change in denomination; overprint "LEGAL TENDER FOR PAYMENT OF ANY AMOUNT" moved down one line from its position on the 500 Mils and One Pound notes.   Circ. $15.00
Crisp $30.00

N-9   TEN PALESTINE POUNDS   Size: 150 x 80mm   Color: red on a yellow-pink background.

FACE :   Same as N-7 except for change in denomination; serial numbers appear in black.

BACK :   Same as N-8 except for change in denomination.   Circ. $22.00
                                                                                              Crisp. ———

N-10   **FIFTY PALESTINE POUNDS**   Size: 159 x 84mm   Color: light violet
             on bluish background.

FACE: Same as N-7 except for change in denomination; serial numbers
        appear in red.

BACK: Same as N-8 except for change in denomination.   RARE

SECOND ISSUE BANKNOTES, BANK LEUMI LE-ISRAEL B.M.—1952

Issued by :	Bank Leumi Le-Israel B.M.
Issued :	June, 1952.
Withdrawn :	1955, gradually being withdrawn; no longer legal tender but redeemable at face value at the Bank of Israel up to February 6, 1981.
Printed by :	American Banknote Company.
Denomination :	Israel Pound (= 1000 Pruta).
Date :	None.
Watermark :	None, metal security planchets in paper.
Designer :	E. L. Hoofien
Serial Nos :	In red or black on face of note.

N-11   500 PRUTA   Size: 148 x 72mm   Color: light olive-green on light blue background.

FACE: In Hebrew above, "BANK LEUMI LE-ISRAEL B.M./WILL PAY TO THE BEARER/500 PRUTA," the denomination appearing within an ornamental design in center which divides the next line, "THE BANK WILL ACCEPT THIS NOTE FOR PAYMENT IN ANY ACCOUNT"; below, "LEGAL TENDER FOR PAYMENT OF ANY AMOUNT" in Hebrew; signature of S. Hoofien to right and A. Barth to left; numeral "500" in each corner, those in the lower corners set at an angle. Serial numbers in red at upper left and right.

BACK: In Arabic above, "BANK LEUMI LE-ISRAEL B.M./WILL PAY TO THE BEARER/FIVE HUNDRED PRUTA," the denomination appearing within an ornamental design in the center which divides "LEGAL TENDER FOR PAYMENT OF ANY AMOUNT" in Arabic on the left and English on the right; below the center design, "THE BANK WILL ACCEPT THIS NOTE FOR PAYMENT IN ANY ACCOUNT" in Arabic; at bottom, "BANK" LEUMI LE-ISRAEL B.M./WILL PAY TO THE BEARER/FIVE HUNDRED PRUTA" and "S. HOOFIEN" to lower left, "A. BARTH" to lower right; within the ornamental frame of the note at the bottom, "THE BANK WILL ACCEPT THIS NOTE FOR PAYMENT IN ANY ACCOUNT" in English. At either side of the center design, the printed signatures of S. Hoofien to the left and A. Barth to the right in Arabic. In each corner, the numeral "50" in Arabic.   Circ. $5.50
                                                                        Crisp $12.50

BANKNOTES — 1952

N-12 **ONE ISRAEL POUND** Size: 150 x 75mm Color: olive-green on pink background.

FACE: Same as N-11 except for change in denomination and numerals in the lower corners are not set at an angle. Serial numbers in black.

BACK: Same as N-11 except for change in denomination and the numeral "1" in Arabic in each corner is set at an angle. Circ. $3.00
Crisp $6.00

BANKNOTES — 1952

N-13   **FIVE ISRAEL POUNDS**   **Size: 155 x 80mm**   **Color: reddish-brown on beige background.**

FACE: Same as N-11 except for change in denomination and numerals "5" are set at an angle. Serial numbers in black.

BACK: Same as N-11 except for change in denomination.   Circ. $7.00
Crisp $15.00

BANKNOTES — 1952

N-14   TEN ISRAEL POUNDS   Size: 155 x 80mm   Color: grey on dark pink background.

FACE :   Same as N-12 except for change in denomination; serial numbers in black.

BACK :   Same as N-11 except for change in denomination.   Circ. $20.00
Crisp $35.00

BANKNOTES — 1952

N-15   **FIFTY ISRAEL POUNDS**   Size: 160 x 85mm   Color: brown on light green background.

FACE: Same as N-12 except for change in denomination; serial numbers in red.

BACK: Same as N-11 except for change in denomination.   Circ. $85.00
Crisp $165.00

BANKNOTES — 1955

THIRD ISSUE BANKNOTES, BANK OF ISRAEL—1955

Issued by:	Bank of Israel.
Issued:	August-October, 1955.
Withdrawn:	1958, gradually being withdrawn.
Printed by:	Thomas de la Rue & Co., Ltd., London
Denomination:	Israel Pound (=1000 Pruta).
Date:	1955/5715.
Watermark:	The Menora (seven-branched candlestick); security metal strip running vertically left of center.
Designer:	An artist from Thomas de la Rue & Co.
Serial Nos:	In black or red on face of note.
Printings:	Face: 1 direct plate and 2 litho-tint printings. Back: 1 direct plate and 1 litho printing.

BANKNOTES — 1955

N-16   **500 PRUTA**   **Size 130 x 72mm**   **Color: red on light blue-green background.**

FACE : Within an ornamental frame incorporating a design of olive leaves and fruit, a view of the ruins of an ancient synagogue at Bir'am; in upper left corner in red, numeral "500" and "PRUTA" in Hebrew; above synagogue in red, "BANK OF ISRAEL" in Hebrew; to left, serial number and date "1955-5715" in black; to right in red, "FIVE HUNDRED PRUTA" in Hebrew; in lower right corner, signature of S. Hoofien and "CHAIRMAN OF THE ADVISORY COUNCIL," signature of David Horowitz and "GOVERNOR OF THE BANK" in Hebrew, and serial number, all in black; in tiny letters at lower left corner, RUINS OF ANCIENT SYNAGOGUE AT BIR'AM"; in upper right corner, cyclamen flower printed in pink and green over the watermark.

BACK : At upper right, numeral "500" and PRUTA in English; at lower left, the same in Arabic; at bottom, "BANK OF ISRAEL" in Arabic to left and English to right; in center, an abstract design resembling an old fashioned gramaphone.

Circ. $2.50
Crisp $5.00

BANKNOTES — 1955

N-17   **ONE ISRAEL POUND**   Size: **135 x 75mm**   Color: **blue tones with pink and orange.**

FACE: Within an ornamental frame incorporating a design of orange leaves and fruit, a view of the Upper Galilee landscape; in upper left corner, the numeral "1"; at upper left and lower right, the serial number in black; at top center, "BANK OF ISRAEL" in Hebrew in blue; at lower right above serial number, "ONE ISRAEL POUND" in blue and the date "1955-5715" in black; at bottom in black, signature of S. Hoofien and "CHAIRMAN OF THE ADVISORY COUNCIL" to left, signature of David Horowitz and "GOVERNOR OF THE BANK" to right; in tiny letters left of the signature, "LANDSCAPE OF UPPER GALILEE" in Hebrew; in upper right corner, an anemone flower printed in blue and pink over the watermark.

BACK: In center, ornamental lettering, "I L 1"; in both upper corners, the numeral "1"; at bottom within an ornamental frame, "BANK OF ISRAEL" in Arabia; above either end of frame, numerals "1" in Arabic; in center, abstract design resembling a sea shell.

Circ. **$2.50**
Crisp **$5.00**

BANKNOTES — 1955

N-18   **FIVE ISRAEL POUNDS**   Size: 140 x78mm   Color: light brown with varicolored background (light green on both ends, blue above and mauve below in center).

FACE :   Within an ornamental frame incorporating a design of grape vines and fruit, a view of the Negev landscape; in upper left corner, the numeral "5"; at upper left and lower right, the serial number in black; at top center, "BANK OF ISRAEL" in Hebrew in brown; to right in brown, "FIVE ISRAEL POUNDS" in Hebrew; at lower right above serial number, signature of S. Hoofien and "CHAIRMAN OF THE ADVISORY COUNCIL" in Hebrew to left, signature of David Horowitz and "GOVERNOR OF THE BANK" in Hebrew to right, both in black; at bottom center, date "1955-5715" in black; in tiny letters below rate, "LANDSCAPE IN THE NEGEV" in Hebrew; in upper right corner, an iris flower printed in lavender over the watermark.

BACK :   Similar to N-17 except for change in denomination and different abstract design, resembling a snail.   Circ. $5.00
Crisp $10.00

BANKNOTES — 1955

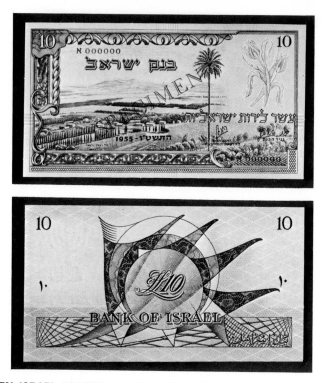

N-19   **TEN ISRAEL POUNDS**   Size: 150 x 82mm   Color: green on a multi-colored background.

FACE: Within an ornamental frame incorporating a design of date clusters, a view of the landscape in the Plain of Jezreel; in the upper left corner, the numeral "10"; at the upper left and lower right, the serial number in black; at top center, "BANK OF ISRAEL" in Hebrew in green; to the right, "TEN ISRAEL POUNDS" in Hebrew in green; to the lower right above the serial number, signature of S. Hoofien and "CHAIRMAN OF THE ADVISORY COUNCIL to left and signature of David Horowitz with "GOVERNOR OF THE BANK" to right, both in Hebrew and in black; at bottom center, the date "1955-5715" in black; in tiny letters to the lower left, "LANDSCAPE IN THE PLAIN OF JEZREEL" in Hebrew; in the upper right corner, a tulip flower printed in red and green over the watermark.

BACK: In the center, ornamental lettering, "I L 10" above "BANK OF ISRAEL" in English; in the upper corners, the numeral "10" with the same Arabic numerals directly below; in the lower right corner, "BANK OF ISRAEL" in Arabic; in the center, an abstract design resembling a starfish.   Circ. $10.00
    Crisp $17.50

BANKNOTES — 1955

N-20   **FIFTY ISRAEL POUNDS**   Size: 160 x 87mm   Color: dark blue-green on a varicolored background.

FACE: Within an ornamental frame on the bottom only which incorporates a design of pomegranates, a view of the road to Jerusalem; in the lower left corner, the numeral "50"; in the upper left and lower right corners, the serial numbers in black and red; at the upper left, "BANK OF ISRAEL" in Hebrew in bluegreen; to the right, in two lines, "FIFTY ISRAEL POUNDS" printed in bluegreen; to the lower right, above the serial number, signature of S. Hoofien and "CHAIRMAN OF THE ADVISORY COUNCIL" to the left and signature of David Horowitz and "GOVERNOR OF THE BANK" to the right, both in Hebrew and in black ink; to the lower left, in black, the date "1955-5715"; in tiny letters below the date, "ROAD TO JERUSALEM" in Hebrew; in the upper right corner, an oleander flower printed in orange and green over the watermark.

BACK: In the upper right corner, ornamental lettering, "I L 50"; in lower right corner, "BANK OF ISRAEL" in Arabic; at bottom center, "BANK OF ISRAEL" in English; to left, numeral "50" in Arabic; in center, an abstract design resembling flying saucers.

Circ. $35.00
Crisp $65.00

BANKNOTES — 1958

FOURTH ISSUE BANKNOTES, BANK OF ISRAEL—1958 and 1960

Issued by :   Bank of Israel.

Issued :   1958 and 1960.

Withdrawn :   Half-Pound being withdrawn since 1963, with Half-Pound coin replacing it.

Printed by :   Enschede, Haarlem, The Netherlands (½, 1, and 50 Pounds), and Thomas de la Rue & Co., Ltd., London (5 and 10 Pounds).

Denomination :   Israel Pound (=100 Agora).

Date :   1958-5718 : ½, 1, 5, 10 Pounds.
                       1960-5720 : 50 Pounds.

Watermark :   The head of the person pictured on the note, but facing the opposite direction of the engraved portrait. Security metal strip running vertically left of center.

Designer :   The brothers Gabriel and Maxim Shamir designed the face of each note and the back of each note except the ½ and 10 Pounds, on which Jacob Zim collaborated with the Shamir Brothers in the design.

Serial Nos :   In red or black on the back of the note.

BANKNOTES — 1958

N-21   ONE HALF ISRAEL POUND   Size: 130 x 72mm   Color: green with an orange wave pattern.

FACE : To left, a girl soldier in uniform with a basket of oranges, against a background of fields, houses, hills, a water tower, and a row of cypress trees; to the right, watermark in an unprinted oval; in upper and lower left corners, small numeral "½"; in upper right corner, large numeral "½"; at top, "BANK OF ISRAEL" in Hebrew; at lower right, "ONE HALF ISRAEL POUND" in Hebrew; at the bottom of the watermark oval, signature of E. I. Nebenzahl and "CHAIRMAN OF THE ADVISORY COUNCIL" in Hebrew to left, signature of David Horowitz and "GOVERNOR OF THE BANK" in Hebrew to the right, and the date "1958-5718" below; to the lower left in tiny letters, "BROTHERS SHAMIR" in Hebrew.

BACK : To the left, the watermark oval; to the right, entrance to the tombs of the Sanhedrin in Jerusalem; "BANK OF ISRAEL" in Hebrew at top, in English vertically on the right end, and in Arabic at the bottom; numeral "½" in English in the upper right corner, in Arabic in the lower right corner; below the vignette in tiny letters, "TOMBS OF THE SANHEDRIN" in Hebrew; at the bottom of the watermark oval, a large numeral "½"; in tiny letters in the lower left corner, "BROTHERS SHAMIR-J. ZIM" in Hebrew; serial number in black at the upper left and lower right.   Crisp $3.00

BANKNOTES — 1958

N-22   **ONE ISRAEL POUND**   **Size: 135 x 75mm**   **Color: blue with faint orange and violet wave patterns.**

FACE: To left, a fisherman against a background of a harbor and mountains with four ships in the bay, a passenger liner, fishing steamer, and two sailboats; to the right, watermark in an unprinted oval; all legends and their positions same as N-21 except for change in denomination, "ONE ISRAEL POUND."

BACK: A mosaic from the floor of an ancient synagogue in Isfiya on Mount Carmel, picturing a stylized wreath with the Hebrew inscription "PEACE BE TO ISRAEL" in the center; in tiny letters below left, "MOSAIC FROM THE ANCIENT SYNAGOGUE IN HUSEIFA" in Hebrew; all legends and their positions same as N-21 except for change in denomination; the designer's name reads "BROTHERS SHAMIR." Serial numbers in red. Crisp $3.00

N-22a   ONE ISRAEL POUND—COMMEMORATIVE ISSUE

As part of Israel's celebrations in 1966 to commemorate the 18th anniversary of statehood, Israel issued at least two new varieties of banknotes. The notes so far involved are the 1 Pound and the 50 Pound notes of the current issue. There is no change in the printing on the notes; even the issue dates (1958 for the 1 Pound, 1960 for the 50 Pound) remain the same. Except the serial numbers on the back of the 1 Pound note are in a greenish-gold instead of in red or black in the normal issue. The main difference lies in the metal strip incorporated into the paper as a security device. In each note the normal security strip has been replaced with a strip in Morse Code, in addition a regular security strip has been added in a different place on the note.

The Morse Code on the 1 Pound note reads "BNQ ISRAL," and is intended as a rendering of the Hebrew for "BANK OF ISRAEL," using the phonetic equivalents in English for the Hebrew letters. The Morse Code security strip may be seen replacing the regular strip at the left end of the note. The new security strip has been added at the center. Crisp $3.00

NOTE: It is not known at this time if the ½, 5 and 10 Pounds of the 1958 issue also exist with the Morse Code security strips.

BANKNOTES — 1958

N-23   **FIVE ISRAEL POUNDS**   **Size: 140 x 78mm**   **Color: brown with orange wave patterns.**

FACE: To the left, a laborer with a sledge hammer against a background of an industrial site; to the right, watermark in an unprinted oval; all legends and their positions same as N-21 except for change in denomination, "FIVE ISRAEL POUNDS."

BACK: An ancient seal of Shema, Minister of Jeroboam II, King of Israel in 787-747 BC, the seal shows a roaring lion with an inscription in ancient Hebrew script reading "OF SHEMA, SERVANT OF JEROBEAM"; below left, in tiny letters, "SEAL OF SHEMA, SERVANT OF JEROBEAM" in Hebrew; all legends and their positions same as N-21 except for change in denomination; the designer's name reads, "BROTHERS SHAMIR." Serial numbers in black.   Crisp $2.25

BANKNOTES — 1958

N-24   **TEN ISRAEL POUNDS**   **Size: 150 x 82mm**   **Color: shades of violet with pink and blue wave patterns.**

FACE: To the left, a scientist with microscope and test tube against a background of laboratory equipment; to the right, watermark in an unprinted oval; all legends and their positions same as N-21 except for change in denomination, "TEN ISRAEL POUNDS."

BACK: One of the Dead Sea Scrolls (showing a passage from Isaiah) and two of the jars in which they were found; below left, in tiny letters, "THE BOOK OF ISAIAH, CHAPTER FORTY" in Hebrew; all legends and their position same as N-21 except for change in denomination; designer's name reads "BROTHERS SHAMIR-J. ZIM." Serial numbers in black.   Crisp $3.50

BANKNOTES — 1960

N-25   **FIFTY ISRAEL POUNDS**   Size: 178 x 93mm   Color: reddish-brown
with green, mauve, and blue wave patterns.

FACE: To the left, two pioneers (Chaluzim), male and female, against
a background of a Negev agricultural settlement; to the right,
a watermark in an oval printed with faint wavy lines; all inscriptions same as N-21 except for change in denomination and date
1960-5720; the denomination "FIFTY ISRAEL POUNDS" in Hebrew moved to the left and date moved between signatures to
allow for larger watermark.

BACK: A mosaic design of a Menora (seven-branched candelabra) discovered in the floor of a recently excavated synagogue of Nirim in
the Negev, to the right of the Menora, a shofar (religious horn)
and ethrog (fruit of the citron tree); to the left a lulab (fruit of
the willow tree) and ethrog; below left, in tiny letters, "ACCORD-
ING TO THE MOSAIC FROM THE ANCIENT SYNAGOGUE
AT NIRIM" in Hebrew; inscriptions same as N-21 except for
denomination change and reversed position from right to left.
Serial numbers in red.   Crisp $18.00

NOTE: Both sides of this note were designed by the Shamir Brothers,
but their name does not appear as on the other notes.

BANKNOTES — 1960

N-25a   FIFTY ISRAEL POUNDS—COMMEMORATIVE ISSUE

Same as N-25a except for the following:
Serial numbers in blue instead of red.

The Morse Code security strip replaces the regular strip near the center of the note, and a new strip has been added to the left end of the note. The Morse Code read "JM ISRAL HI" and is intended as a rendering of the Hebrew for "AM ISRAEL HAI" (the People of Israel live on), using the phonetic equivalents in English for the Hebrew letters. This was the motto of the 18th anniversary year, and figured prominently on the silver 5 Pound Commemorative issued in 1966-5726 (C-17).   Crisp $25.00

FIFTH ISSUE BANKNOTES, BANK OF ISRAEL

The third issue by the Bank of Israel will consist of the following denominations: 5, 10, 50, and 100 Pounds, eliminating the ½ and 1 Pound notes now being replaced with coins. This series will be characterized by portraits of outstanding Jewish personalities.

N-26	5 Pounds	Professor Albert Einstein
N-27	10 Pounds	Poet Chaim Nachman Bialik
N-28	50 Pounds	President Chaim Weizmann
N-29	100 Pounds	Dr. Theodor Herzl

REFERENCE CHART TO KADMAN NUMBERS

PRUTA		AGORA		COMMEMORATIVES	
P-1	K-1	A-101	K-35	C-1	K-3-4
P-2	K-2	A-101a	—	C-2	K-7-8
P-3	K-3	A-101b	—	C-3	K-12-13
P-4	K-5	A-102	K-40	C-4	K-16-17
P-4a	K-4	A-102a	—	C-5	K-20-21
P-5	K-6	A-102b	K-41	C-6	—
P-6	K-8	A-103	K-47	C-7	K-24-25
P-6a	K-7	A-103a	—	C-8	K-26-27
P-7	K-9	A-104	K-51	C-9	K-1-2
P-8	K-11	A-104a	—	C-10	K-5-6
P-8a	K-10	A-105	—	C-11	K-9-10
P-9	K-25	A-106	—	C-12	K-14-15
P-10	K-26	A-107	—	C-13	K-18-19
P-11	K-27	A-108	—	C-14	K-22-23
P-12	K-12	A-201	K-37	C-15	—
P-13	K-14	A-202	K-42	C-16	—
P-13a	K-13	A-202a	K-43	C-17	—
P-14	K-28	A-203	K-48	C-18	—
P-15	K-15	A-203a	—		
P-16	K-17	A-204	K-52	**ISRAEL'S**	
P-16a	K-16	A-205	—	**BANKNOTES**	
P-17	K-30	A-206	—	N-1	K-F1
P-18	K-29	A-207	—	N-2	K-F2
P-19	K-31	A-208	—	N-3	K-F3
P-20	K-18	A-301	K-38	N-4	K-F4
P-20a	K-19	A-302	K-44	N-5	K-F5
P-21	K-34	A-302a	K-45	N-6	K-1
P-22	K-32	A-303	K-49	N-7	K-2
P-23	K-33	A-303a	—	N-8	K-3
P-24	K-21	A-304	K-53	N-9	K-4
P-25	K-22	A-305	—	N-10	K-5
P-26	K-23	A-305a	—	N-11	K-6
P-27	K-24	A-306	—	N-12	K-7
		A-307	—	N-13	K-8
		A-308	—	N-14	K-9
GOLD		A-401	K-39	N-15	K-10
C-1	K-11	A-402	K-46	N-16	K-11
C-2	K-28	A-403	K-50	N-17	K-12
C-3	K-29	A-404	K-54	N-18	K-13
C-4	—	A-405	—	N-19	K-14
C-4a	—	A-406	—	N-20	K-15
		A-407	—	N-21	K-16
		A-501	K-55	N-21a	—
		A-502	—	N-22	K-17
		A-503	—	N-22a	—
		A-504	—	N-23	K-18
		A-505	—	N-23a	—
		A-601	K-56	N-24	K-19
		A-602	—	N-24a	—
		A-603	—	N-25	K-20
		A-604	—	N-25a	—

PALESTINE SECTION

BRITISH MANDATORY COINS OF PALESTINE

Palestine was a part of the Turkish empire in 1917, when it was captured by British troops. It remained under British military administration until July 24, 1924, when it became a British Mandate under the League of Nations. The mandate was abolished at midnight, May 14, 1948, when Israel became an independent state.

A great variety of coins—Turkish, Egyptian, French, and English—were used in world trade in Palestine in 1917, although Turkish coins were most widely used. In 1924, Britain introduced Egyptian currency to replace that of Turkey until 1927, when a local currency was issued.

A committee was established by the British, composed of Arabs and Jews, to select a suitable name for the proposed new coinage of Palestine. On February 7, 1927, the Currency Board of Palestine announced that the new coinage of Palestine would be in "Mil" denominations. The Palestine Pound was to be the equivalent of a British gold sovereign (20 shillings) and was divided into 1000 Mils.

The first coins were placed in circulation on November 1, 1927, and were minted at the Royal Mint in London. The 100 and 50 Mils were issued in .720 fine silver, the 20, 10, and 5 Mils were issued in cupronickel (and in bronze during World War II, 1942-1944), and the 2 and 1 Mils were issued in bronze.

The coins were struck from 1927 to 1947; the 1947 issue of 1, 2, 5 and 10 Mils was never released. The entire issue was melted down except for specimens in the British Museum and the Ashmolean Museum in Oxford. A portion of the 1927 coins was later returned to the Royal Mint and melted down.

Proofs were struck in various years, and there should exist 33 proof sets of the 1927 issue in cases containing two of each denomination.

The British Mandatory coins of Palestine remained legal tender in Israel until September 15, 1948; in Jordan until June 30, 1951; and in Egypt until June 9, 1951.

On the obverse of each denomination are two Hebrew letters in brackets following the Hebrew word "PALESTINE"; these two letters are the abbreviation of "LAND OF ISRAEL." When the coins were released in 1927, the Hebrew inscription incited the Arabs to protest, as they thought that too much priority had been given to the Hebrew script. The fact that the coins were released on the eve of the anniversary of the Balfour Declaration (which favored the establishment of a national home for the Jews in Palestine) provoked the Arabs into the belief that Britain had sinister designs on Palestine. This belief was to be disproved at a later date when Britain fought the partition of Palestine into Jewish and Arab states when the issue came before the United Nations Assembly.

There are 59 coins needed to complete the Palestine series by date. They are very difficult to obtain in uncirculated condition and proofs are exceedingly rare, therefore values are shown for average circulated condition only. A gem uncirculated specimen would command a price of from five to ten times higher than the quotes here. The low mintages of the 20 Mils coins make this the hardest denomination to obtain. Taking into consideration that the coinage has been obsolete since 1948 and that the greatest portion of the coins has been melted, collecting British Mandatory coins of Palestine in choice condition is quite a challenge. Specimens have been known to be counterfeited.

OTTOMAN TURKISH COINAGE USED IN PALESTINE — 1917

The issues of Mohammed V (1909-1918, AH 1327 accession date) were used in Palestine at the time of the British capture. The monetary unit of the Ottoman Empire was the Turkish Piastre of 40 Paras or 100 Aspres. The following coins were in circulation in 1917. The Arabic words "RESHAT" or "EL-GHAZI" are found to the right of the Toughra.

DENOMINATION	METAL	YEARS (1327+)	TOUGHRA	
5 Para	Nickel	3-7	"Reshat"	
10 Paras	Nickel	2-8	"Reshat"	
20 Paras	Nickel	2-6	"Reshat"	
40 Paras	Nickel	3-5	"Reshat"	
*40 Paras	Cupronickel	8	"El-Ghazi"	
1 Piastre	.830 fine silver	1-7	"Reshat"	
*2 Piastres	.830 fine silver	1-7	"Reshat"	
*5 Piastres	.830 fine silver	1-7	"Reshat"	
10 Piastres	.830 fine silver	1-7	"Reshat"	
20 Piastres	.830 fine silver	1, 9	"El-Ghazi"	
12½ Piastres	.9166 fine gold	7-13	"El-Ghazi"	
25 Piastres	.9166 fine gold	7-13	"El-Ghazi"	
50 Piastres	.9166 fine gold	7-13	"El-Ghazi"	
*100 Piastres	.9166 fine gold	7-13	"El-Ghazi"	
250 Piastres	.9166 fine gold	7-13	"El-Ghazi"	
500 Piastres	.9166 fine gold	7-13	"El-Ghazi"	

Gold pieces were also struck in the years 1-7 from 25 to 500 Piastres with the "Reshat," they are quite rare.

One Piastre was also known as one Girsh and 100 Piastres as one Lira. The coins were struck at Constantinople.

To find the date of issue on a Turkish coin (in terms of the Moslem calendar), add one less than the regnal year (given here under the "Years" column) to the accession year (in this case, 1327 AH). To convert your computed date of 1333 to an AD date, subtract 3% of the AH date from the AH date and add 622. In this example, the coin was struck in 1915. On these coins, the regnal year is found in Arabic below the Toughra; the accession date is found, also in Arabic, on the opposite side.

COINAGE OF EGYPT UNDER THE BRITISH PROTECTORATE (1914-1922) USED IN PALESTINE 1924-1927

The issues of Sultan Hussein Kamil of Egypt (1915-1917) under the British Protectorate, were used in Palestine until the Palestine Currency Board coins were ready for distribution in 1927. The British outlawed Turkish coinage and substituted the Egyptian coinage for this period.

Denomination	Metal	Year	
*½ Millieme	Bronze	1917	
* 1 Millieme	Cupronickel	1916-1917	
* 2 Milliemes	Cupronickel	1916-1917	
5 Milliemes	Cupronickel	1916-1917	
10 Milliemes	Cupronickel	1916-1917	
2 Piastres	Silver	1916-1917	
5 Piastres	Silver	1916-1917	
10 Piastres	Silver	1916-1917	
*20 Piastres	Silver	1916-1917	
*100 Piastres	Gold	1916	

The cupronickel coins were struck at the Heaton Mint in Birmingham and at the King's Norton Mint. Mintmarks "H" or "KN" are on the reverse. The bronze, silver, and gold coins were struck at Cairo.

PALESTINE MANDATE COINS
ONE MIL

OBV: "PALESTINE" in Arabic, English, and Hebrew; date below in English and Arabic numerals.

REV: In center, seven-leaved olive branch dividing numerals "1" in English on left, in Arabic on right; above, "ONE MIL" in English, "MIL" to left in Hebrew, to right in Arabic.

Edge: Plain; Diameter 21mm; Weight 3.23 gm.

	Year	ALLOY			Mintage	Circ.
PMC-1	1927	.955 copper, .015 zinc, .030 tin			10,000,000	.50
PMC-1a	1927 Proof	''	''	''	—	—
PMC-2	1935	''	''	''	704,000	5.00
PMC-3	1937	''	''	''	1,200,000	2.00
PMC-4	1939	''	''	''	3,700,000	.50
PMC-4a	1939 Proof	''	''	''	—	—
PMC-5	1940	''	''	''	396,000	6.00
PMC-6	1941	''	''	''	1,920,000	1.00
PMC-7	1942	.970 copper, .025 zinc, .005 tin			4,480,000	.50
PMC-8	1943	''	''	''	2,800,000	.50
PMC-9	1944	''	''	''	1,440,000	.75
PMC-10	1946	.955 copper, .015 zinc, .030 tin			1,632,000	1.00
PMC-10a	1946 Proof	''	''	''	—	—
	1947	NEVER RELEASED			2,880,000	—

TWO MILS

OBV: "PALESTINE" in Arabic, English, and Hebrew; date below in English and Arabic numerals.

REV: In center, seven-leaved olive branch dividing numerals "2" on left in English, in Arabic on right; above, "TWO MILS" in English, "MILS" to left in Hebrew, to right in Arabic.

Edge: Plain; Diameter 26mm; Weight 7.77 gm.

	Year	ALLOY	Mintage	Circ.
PMC-11	1927	.955 copper, .015 zinc, .030 tin	5,000,000	.50
PMC-11a	1927 Proof	" " "	—	—
PMC-12	1941	" " "	1,600,000	.75
PMC-12a	1941 Proof	" " "	—	—
PMC-13	1942	.970 copper, .025 zinc, .005 tin	2,400,000	.75
PMC-14	1945	" " "	960,000	1.00
PMC-15	1946	.955 copper, .015 zinc, .030 tin	960,000	1.00
	1947	NEVER RELEASED	480,000	—

FIVE MILS

OBV: Around central hole, a wreath of olive leaves surounded by "PALES-TINE" in English above, Hebrew to left, and Arabic to right; below, the date in English and Arabic numerals.

REV: Around central hole, inscriptions "5 MILS" in English, Arabic, and Hebrew, the numeral 5 of the English phrase at top.

Edge: Plain; Diameter 20mm; Weight 2.91 gm.

	Year	ALLOY		Mintage	Circ.
PMC-16	1927	.750 copper, .250 nickel		10,000,000	.50
PMC-16a	1927 Proof	''	''	—	—
PMC-17	1934	''	''	500,000	5.00
PMC-18	1935	''	''	2,700,000	.75
PMC-19	1939	''	''	2,000,000	.75
PMC-19a	1939 Proof	''	''	—	—
PMC-20	1941	''	''	400,000	6.50
PMC-20a	1941 Proof	''	''	—	—
PMC-21	1942	.970 copper, .025 zinc, .005 tin		2,700,000	.75
PMC-22	1944	''	'' ''	1,000,000	.75
PMC-23	1946	.750 copper, .250 nickel		1,000,000	.75
PMC-23a	1946 Proof	''	''	—	—
	1947	NEVER RELEASED		1,000,000	—

TEN MILS

OBV: Central hole with the date above in English and below in Arabic
numerals; "PALESTINE" in English above, Hebrew to left, and
Arabic to right.

REV: Central hole surrounded by wreath of olive leaves; inscriptions
around, "10 MILS" in English, Arabic, and Hebrew, with numeral
10 of the English phrase at the top.

Edge: Plain; Diameter 27mm; Weight 6.47 gm.

	Year	ALLOY	Mintage	Circ.
PMC-24	1927	.750 copper, .250 nickel	5,000,000	1.00
PMC-24a	1927 Proof	'' ''	—	—
PMC-25	1933	'' ''	500,000	6.00
PMC-25a	1933 Proof	'' ''	—	—
PMC-26	1934	'' ''	500,000	6.00
PMC-26a	1934 Proof	'' ''	—	—
PMC-27	1935	'' ''	1,150,000	1.50
PMC-27a	1935 Proof	'' ''	—	—
PMC-28	1937	'' ''	750,000	4.00
PMC-28a	1937 Proof	'' ''	—	—
PMC-29	1939	'' ''	1,000,000	1.50
PMC-29a	1939 Proof	'' ''	—	—
PMC-30	1940	'' ''	1,500,000	1.25
PMC-30a	1940 Proof	'' ''	—	—
PMC-31	1941	'' ''	400,000	5.00
PMC-31a	1941 Proof	'' ''	—	—
PMC-32	1942	'' ''	600,000	4.00
PMC-33	1942	.970 copper, .025 zinc, .005 tin	1,000,000	1.50
PMC-34	1943	'' '' ''	1,000,000	1.50
PMC-35	1946	.750 copper, .250 nickel	1,000,000	1.50
PMC-35a	1946 Proof	'' ''	—	—
	1947	NEVER RELEASED	1,000,000	—

TWENTY MILS

OBV: Central hole with date above in English and below in Arabic numerals; "PALESTINE" in English above, Hebrew to left, and Arabic to right.

REV: Central hole with inscriptions around, "20 MILS" in English, Arabic, and Hebrew, with the numeral 20 of the English phrase at top.

Edge: Plain; Diameter 30.5mm; Weight 11.33 gm.

	Year	ALLOY	Mintage	Circ.
PMC-36	1927	.750 copper, .250 nickel	1,500,000	3.00
PMC-36a	1927 Proof	'' ''	—	—
PMC-37	1933	'' ''	250,000	6.00
PMC-38	1934	'' ''	125,000	25.00
PMC-39	1935	'' ''	575,000	3.50
PMC-40	1940	'' ''	200,000	11.00
PMC-40a	1940 Proof	'' ''	—	—
PMC-41	1941	'' ''	100,000	40.00
PMC-41a	1941 Proof	'' ''	—	—
PMC-42	1942	.970 copper, .025 zinc, .005 tin	1,100,000	2.50
PMC-43	1944	'' '' ''	1,000,000	2.75

FIFTY MILS

OBV: Within a circle, an olive branch with four leaves dividing dates in English to the left, in Arabic numerals to the right; inscriptions around circle, "PALESTINE" in English above, Hebrew to left, and Arabic to right.

REV: Numerals "50" in Arabic at top, in English at bottom, with "FIFTY MILS" written out between in Arabic, English, and Hebrew.

Edge: Milled; Diameter 23.6mm; Weight 5.83 gm.

	Year	ALLOY		Mintage	Circ.
PMC-44	1927	.720 silver, .280 copper		8,000,000	2.00
PMC-44a	1927 Proof	''	''	—	—
PMC-45	1931	''	''	500,000	7.00
PMC-46	1933	''	''	1,000,000	3.50
PMC-47	1934	''	''	398,861	10.00
PMC-48	1935	''	''	5,600,000	2.25
PMC-49	1939	''	''	3,000,000	2.50
PMC-49a	1939 Proof	''	''	—	—
PMC-50	1940	''	''	2,000,000	2.75
PMC-50a	1940 Proof	''	''	—	—
PMC-51	1942	''	''	5,000,000	2.25

ONE HUNDRED MILS

OBV: Seven-leaved olive branch dividing dates in English numerals to left, in Arabic numerals to right; surrounding inscriptions, "PALES-TINE" in English above, Hebrew to left, and Arabic to right.

REV: Within central circle, numerals "100" in English numerals above, in Arabic numerals below; around circle, "ONE HUNDRED MILS" written out in English above, in Hebrew to left, and in Arabic to right.

Edge: Milled; Diameter 29mm; Weight 11.66 gm.

	Year	ALLOY		Mintage	Circ.
PMC-52	1927	.720 silver, .280 copper		2,000,000	2.50
PMC-52a	1927 Proof	"	"	—	—
PMC-53	1931	"	"	250,000	10.00
PMC-53a	1931 Proof	"	"	—	—
PMC-54	1933	"	"	500,000	7.00
PMC-55	1934	"	"	200,000	12.50
PMC-56	1935	"	"	2,850,000	2.50
PMC-57	1939	"	"	1,500,000	3.00
PMC-57a	1939 Proof	"	"	—	—
PMC-58	1940	"	"	1,000,000	3.50
PMC-59	1942	"	"	2,500,000	2.50

BANKNOTES OF THE PALESTINE CURRENCY BOARD

The Palestine Currency Board was appointed in 1926 by the British Secretary of State for the Colonies. This board was in charge of the introduction and control of currency in Palestine under the British Mandate. The activities of this board were confined to the issue of currency notes, which were covered by the like amount of Sterling in London. The board was completely independent of local government authority. On February 7, 1927, the board created the Palestine Pound, which was divided into 1000 Mils.

After the proposals of the United Nations to partition Palestine into Jewish and Arab states, Britain removed Palestine from the Sterling bloc in February of 1948. This action changed the Palestine Currency Board notes into foreign currency, and the balance of Palestine Sterling was frozen by the British government.

The Palestine Currency Board notes were issued in denominations of 500 Mils, 1, 5, 10, 50, and 100 Palestine Pounds. These notes were issued and redeemed as a virtually continuous process from November 1, 1927, when they were first introduced, until the termination of the mandate in 1948. The number of notes issued reached its peak in May of 1948, when 59,605,333,500 Palestine Pounds were in circulation.

When the British Mandate came to a close on May 15, 1948, the Palestine Currency Board and its currency system ceased to function. When the British left Palestine, they failed to make any provisional arrangement with the new state of Israel concerning the currency. This was not an oversight, but a deliberate rebuke indicating British resentment of the partition of Palestine.

The Palestine Currency Board notes were printed by Thomas de la Rue & Co. of London. The notes ceased to be legal tender in the countries where they were in circulation on the following dates:

Israel: September 15, 1958

Jordan: September 30, 1950 (notes only)
June 30, 1951 (coins)

Egypt: June 9, 1951 (Gaza Strip)

The following gentlemen served as members of the Palestine Currency Board at various times; their names are readily identified on the notes. The earliest appointments to the board are listed first.

Sir Percy Ezechial	H. F. Downie	J. B. Williams
L. Couper	E. B. Boyd	H. T. Bourdillion
A. J. Harding	S. Caine	J. Gutch
R. V. Vernon	R. N. Kershaw	D. N. Brinson
Sir John Caulcutt	J. Trafford Smith	J. M. Hunter

PALESTINE CURRENCY BOARD NOTES

Issued by :	Palestine Currency Board, London.
Issue Dates :	1927-1948.
Withdrawn :	September 15, 1948.
Printed by :	Thomas de la Rue & Co. Ltd., London
Denomination :	Palestine Pound (divided into 1000 Mils).
Watermark :	Ornamental design with an olive branch.
Serial Numbers :	In black or red on face of note.
Printings :	One litho-tint and two direct plate workings.

PALESTINE CURRENCY BOARD NOTES

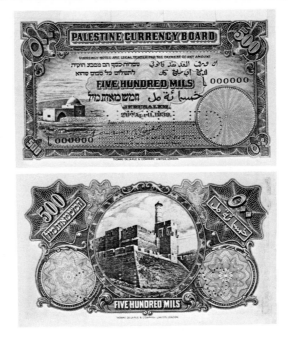

PCB-1   500 MILS   Size: 127 x 76 mm

FACE : At top, "PALESTINE CURRENCY BOARD/CURRENCY NOTES
ARE LEGAL TENDER FOR THE PAYMENT OF ANY
AMOUNT" in English, the second line in small letters; directly
below, legends repeated in Hebrew to left and in Arabic to right;
denomination "FIVE HUNDRED MILS" in English and directly
below in Hebrew to left and Arabic to right; "JERUSALEM" and
date of issue in two lines directly below denomination; three signatures and "MEMBERS OF THE PALESTINE CURRENCY
BOARD" at bottom; numeral "500" in English in lower left and
upper right corners, in Arabic in upper left and lower right corners; imprint "THOMAS DE LA RUE & COMPANY, LIMITED,
LONDON" on bottom margin. Vignette of the Tomb of Rachel
near Hebron to left; watermark within circle covered with printed
lathework design at right. Serial number in black below vignette
and above watermark. Color: chrome green and purple.

BACK : In center, vignette of King David's Tower and Citadel in Jerusalem within circle, watermark within circle as on face to left,
circular lathework design on right. Denomination "FIVE HUN-
DRED MILS" within frame in English below vignette, in Hebrew
at an angle under the numeral "1" in the upper left corner, and
in Arabic at an angle under the Arabic numeral "1" in the upper
right corner. Imprint "THOMAS DE LA RUE & COMPANY,
LIMITED, LONDON" on bottom margin. Color: purple.

Circ. $25.00

PALESTINE CURRENCY BOARD NOTES

PCB-2   **ONE PALESTINE POUND**   **Size: 166 x 89 mm**

FACE: Same as PCB-1 except for denomination "ONE PALESTINE
        POUND," numeral "1" at corners, and vignette of Omar Mosque
        in Jerusalem (also called the Dome of the Rock) to left. Colors:
        yellow, purple, green, and black.

BACK: Same as PCB-1 except with the addition of olive branches at
        either side of the central vignette, and denomination "ONE
        PALESTINE POUND" within frame in English below vignette,
        Hebrew superimposed on the numeral "1" in the upper left corner,
        and in Arabic superimposed on the Arabic numeral "1" in the
        upper right corner. Color: green.   Circ. $20.00

PALESTINE CURRENCY BOARD NOTES

PCB-3 **FIVE PALESTINE POUNDS** **Size: 191 x 102 mm**

FACE: Same as PCB-1 except for denomination "FIVE PALESTINE POUNDS," numeral "5" at corners, and vignette of Crusaders' Tower at Ramleh to left. Serial numbers in red. Colors: green, purple, red, and black.

BACK: Same as PCB-2 except ornamental lathework design flanked by olive branches (instead of olive branches alone) surrounds vignette, change in denomination to "FIVE PALESTINE POUNDS," and written-out denominations in Hebrew above watermark and in Arabic above circular design not superimposed over numerals but placed directly below the numerals. Colors: green and red.

Circ. $65.00

PALESTINE CURRENCY BOARD NOTES

PCB-4 **TEN PALESTINE POUNDS** Size: **191 x 102 mm**

FACE: Same as PCB-2 except for denomination, "TEN PALESTINE POUNDS." Serial numbers in red. Colors: green, brown, blue, and black.

BACK: Same as PCB-3 except for denomination, "TEN PALESTINE POUNDS." Colors: green and blue. Circ. $135.00

PALESTINE CURRENCY BOARD NOTES

PCB-5   **FIFTY PALESTINE POUNDS**   **Size: 191 x 102 mm**

FACE: Same as PCB-3 except denomination, "FIFTY PALESTINE
        POUNDS." Serial numbers in red. Colors: green, brown, purple
        and black.

BACK: Same as PCB-3 except denomination, "FIFTY PALESTINE
        POUNDS." Colors: green and purple.   Circ. $400.00

PALESTINE CURRENCY BOARD NOTES

PCB-6 **ONE HUNDRED PALESTINE POUNDS**   **Size: 191 x 102 mm**

FACE: Same as PCB-3 except denomination, "ONE HUNDRED PALES-TINE POUNDS." Serial numbers in red. Colors: brown, green, and black.

BACK: Same as PCB-3 except denomination, "ONE HUNDRED PALES-TINE POUNDS." Colors: grey and green.   **RARE**

MEDAL SECTION

INDEX TO THE MEDALS OF ISRAEL

MEDALS OF ISRAEL

The significant events in the development of the State of Israel have been recorded in a unique and beautiful form through the medium of State Medals. The Bank of Israel, which is the exclusive authority to mint coins for the state, was entrusted with the task of minting commemorative coins. In 1958, the Israel government resolved to mark the tenth anniversary of Israel by striking a special medal along with the five pound silver commemorative coin.

The Anniversary Committee nominated by the Prime Minister struck the first medals of Israel in bronze, silver, and gold—the "Judaea Capta—Israel Liberata" medals. The medals were received with enormous enthusiasm, and were sold out within a few weeks. In view of the great success of this first experiment, it was decided to continue the issue of suitable medals and to place this task with a special department of the Prime Minister's Office. In 1962 this department was organized into the Israel Government Coins and Medals Corporation Ltd., a government-owned concern.

Medals have been struck in commemoration of historical or outstanding persons and events and on the occasions of international congresses, conventions, competitions, etc., the latter intended mainly to be dedicated to the participants.

Medal issues are always struck in bronze or copper, usually in silver, and occasionally in gold. Copper has been used for only four issues, the remainder of the base-metal issues being struck in red or yellow bronze, the former having a greater copper content than the latter. In Israel government releases, the yellow bronze used is sometimes referred to as tombac.

Each medal issue by the corporation is approved by a public committee especially commissioned by the Prime Minister. The task of the committee is to decide first on the character of a given medal, and then choose the best design submitted. The corporation is headed by a director-general responsible to a board of directors, which represents the Prime Minister's office, the ministries of finance, commerce, and industry, the Bank of Israel, the Ministry of Tourism, and the Ministry of Foreign Affairs.

All the shares in the corporation are held by the government of Israel, and profits from sales are devoted to the restoration and preservation of archaeological sites.

The medals may be purchased directly from the corporation in Israel, and beautiful albums are available for their housing. Nearly all issues still are available at the issue price, therefore in this catalogue the only price given is the original price of issue. The address of the corporation is Israel Government Coins and Medals Corporation Ltd., 11 Keren Hayesod Street, Jerusalem, Israel.

MEDAL OF LIBERATION: "JUDAEA CAPTA—ISRAEL LIBERATA" M-1

The first medal of the State of Israel was issued in 1958 by the Tenth Anniversary of Israel Committee. This medal symbolizes the turning point from bondage to freedom for the Jewish people in their own state. Designed by Ote Wallisch from a sketch by Dr. Leo Kadman.

M-1

OBV: In the center, a replica of a Roman coin commemorating the Roman victory in the Jewish-Roman war of AD 66-70; around the rim a chain broken by "EXILE OF JUDAEA" above and the date "3830" below, both in Hebrew. The coin pictures a palmtree with seven branches, symbolizing Judaea; on the right, a seated Jewess representing the Jewish people, in an attitude of dejection; on the left, a Jewish captive with his hands bound behind his back; inscription above, "JUDAEA CAPTA," initials in exergue, "S C" (for Senatus Consulto, by decree of the Senate).

REV: In the center, a palmtree symbolizing the land of Israel; to left, a standing Israeli woman holding a sheaf of corn; to right, an Israeli worker; inscription in Latin on right and left, "ISRAEL LIBERATA," inscriptions in Hebrew, "JERUSALUM" in exergue, "TEN YEARS FREEDOM OF ISRAEL" above, date "5718" (1958) below.

Edge: Incuse, "ISRAEL GOVERNMENT APPROVED ISSUE 1948-1958" between two State emblems.

NOTE: This medal in actuality was issued by Jacob Japhet Co., Bankers with the blessings of the Government of Israel.

Number	Date	Metal	Diameter	Weight	Mintage	Issue Price
M-1	1958	Gold	27mm	15 gm.	10,000	—
M-1a	1958	Silver	38mm	30 gm.	10,000	—

MEDAL OF LIBERATION CONT.

M-1b

OBV: In center, a Roman Judaea Capta coin of different type than M-1 on which, to the left of the palmtree, the Emperor stands in triumph; around is a chain broken at the bottom by "EXILE OF JUDAEA 3830" in Hebrew.

REV: In center, a palmtree; to left, a standing Israeli woman lifting her infant to the sun with joy; to right, an Israeli worker planting a sapling; Latin inscription above, "ISRAEL LIBERATA"; Hebrew inscription below, "TEN YEARS FREEDOM OF ISRAEL "5719."

Edge: Incuse, miniature emblem of the State of Israel and "STATE OF ISRAEL" in Hebrew and English.

Obverse and reverse designed by Rothschild and Lippmann.

Number	Date	Metal	Diameter	Weight	Mintage	Issue Price
M-1b	1958	Copper	61mm	105 gm.	25,000	—
M-1c	1961	.935 fine silver	35mm	30 gm.	5,000	8.00
M-1d	1961	.935 fine silver	61mm	115 gm.	3,000	29.50

MEDAL OF VALOUR   M-2

The second medal, struck in the year of the Tenth Anniversary, was intended to symbolize the gallantry of those who fought to establish a free and independent Israel. Designed by Rothschild and Lippmann.

OBV: Right, a sword with an olive branch, emblem of the Israel Defense Army; in the field, "PEACE BE WITHIN THY WALLS" in Hebrew with source "PSALMS CXXII/7" in small incuse Hebrew letters directly below; around rim to left, same verse in English with source incuse in small letters to right of sword.

REV: Right, the roaring lion statue at Tel-Hai (erected in homage to the heroic stand of Yosef Trumpeldor and his comrades when the settlement was surrounded by Arab guerillas in 1921); to left in field, "FOR THE BUILDERS EVERY ONE HAD HIS SWORD GIRDED BY HIS SIDE" in Hebrew; same verse repeated in English to left around rim; source of verse "NEHEMIAH IV/12" in English and Hebrew to right of lion.

Edge: Incuse, a miniature emblem of the State and "STATE of ISRAEL" in Hebrew and English on the large silver medal, in Hebrew only on the other medals.

Number	Date	Metal	Diameter	Weight	Mintage	Issue Price
M-2	1959	Copper	60mm	134 gm.	75,000	4.50
M-2a	1959	.935 fine silver	35mm	30 gm.	25,000	8.00
M-2b	1962	.935 fine silver	60mm	117 gm.	3,000	29.50

B'NAI B'RITH CONVENTION MEDAL   M-3

The third medal was struck during the Tenth Anniversary Year in honor of the World Convention of the order of B'nai B'rith, which took place in Jerusalem in May of 1959. By holding its convention in the capital of Israel, this great Jewish brotherhood testified that its order recognizes the unity of the Jewish people centered upon Israel. Designed by Zvi Narkiss.

OBV: Above, the emblem of the Tenth Anniversary celebration, composed of the word "ISRAEL," the numeral "10," and the seven-branched Menora; in center, TENTH ANNIVERSARY OF ISRAEL'S IN-DEPENDENCE, 5719" in Hebrew in three lines; around rim, ISRAEL'S TENTH ANNIVERSARY YEAR, 1958-1959" in English.

REV: Above, the seven-branched Menora; below, "WORLD CONVEN-TION OF B'NAI B'RITH, YEAR 5719" in Hebrew in four lines and the date "May 25-29, 1959" in English; around rim, B'NAI B'RITH CONVENTION" in English.

Edge: Incuse, a miniature emblem of the State and "STATE OF ISRAEL" in Hebrew and English.

Number	Date	Metal	Diameter	Weight	Mintage	Issue Price
M-3	1959	Copper	61mm	103 gm.	10,000	4.50
M-3a	1961	.935 fine silver	35mm	29.5 gm.	3,000	8.00

TEL-AVIV JUBILEE MEDAL   M-4

The fourth medal, struck in 1959, was in honor of the Jubilee of Tel-Aviv. It was intended to record the titanic development since the first building went up on the bare sands of the Mediterranean shore, up to the present day. Tel-Aviv is a hub of business and artistic life, a city of transcendent ebullience with a cosmopolitan air. Designed by Zvi Narkiss.

OBV: The original, unpeopled dunes of Tel-Aviv and the waves of the sea; right, the shield of David; left, "THOUGH THY BEGINNING WAS SMALL, YET THY LATTER END SHALL GREATLY IN-CREASE" in Hebrew; around the rim the same verse in English and the source, "JOB 8:7," in Hebrew and English.

REV: Stylized view of Tel-Aviv today, depicted schematically with houses and streets; right, "TEL-AVIV, 5669-5769" in Hebrew in three lines with an olive branch alongside; below, "TEL-AVIV, 1909-1959" in English.

Edge: Incuse, a miniature emblem of the State and "THE STATE OF ISRAEL" in Hebrew and English.

Number	Date	Metal	Diameter	Weight	Mintage	Issue Price
M-4	1959	Bronze	59mm	121 gm.	45,000	4.50
M-4a	1959	.935 fine silver	35mm	30 gm.	25,000	8.00

FIRST INTERNATIONAL HARP COMPETITION MEDAL   M-5

The fifth medal was struck in testimony of the first International Harp Competition held in Jerusalem in September, 1959. Thus was revived an ancient tradition in Jewish annals. On religious occasions the harp was frequently in evidence; it was conspicuous in the van of thanksgiving processions to the Temple. The harp appears on a coin associated with the victory of Bar-Kochba over the Romans (AD 132-135). Harpists from all corners of the world gathered in Jerusalem to figure in the competition. All who took part were presented with a copper medal as a souvenir. This medal (in copper) is not for sale. Designed by F. Pauker.

OBV: In the center, a standing figure of King David playing a harp; to right, "INTERNATIONAL HARP COMPETITION" in Hebrew; to left, following rim, "JERUSALEM, 5719" in Hebrew.

REV: In center, the word "HARP" in Hebrew, its middle letter contrived in the outline of a harp; below "PRESENTED BY THE COMMITTEE OF THE HARP FESTIVAL OF ISRAEL" in French; above, "FIRST INTERNATIONAL HARP COMPETITION" and below, "JERUSALEM, ISRAEL, SEPTEMBER 1959" in French, following curve of rim.

Edge: Incuse, a miniature emblem of the State and "THE STATE OF ISRAEL" in Hebrew and English.

Number	Date	Metal	Diameter	Weight	Mintage	Issue Price
M-5	1959	Copper	61mm	100 gm.	100	NFS
M-5a	1961	.935 fine silver	35mm	30 gm.	3,000	8.00

HADASSAH MEDAL   M-6

The sixth medal was struck in honor of the dedication of the Hadassah Medical Center in August of 1960. Hadassah, the Women's Zionist Organization of America, made possible the building of this temple of healing on the outskirts of Jerusalem, where anyone, regardless of creed, color, or origin, may come for treatment from Israel and beyond. The Medical Center comprises the Hadassah-Hebrew University Hospital and outpatient department, a school and living quarters for nurses, and precincts for the Hebrew University-Hadassah Medical School. Designed by Miriam Karoli.

M-6a

OBV: Within an incuse square with rounded corners, a nurse holding a child, the Hadassah emblem in the upper left corner of the square.

REV: A representation of the Hadassah Medical Center; below in English, "HADASSAH HEBREW UNIVERSITY / MEDICAL CENTRE, JERUSALEM" and, in smaller letters, "DEDICATION AUGUST 1960"; surrounding inscription in Hebrew, "HADASSAH MEDICAL CENTER AND THE HEBREW UNIVERSITY, JERUSALEM."

Edge: Incuse, a miniature emblem of the State and "THE STATE OF ISRAEL" in Hebrew and English.

Number	Date	Metal	Diameter	Weight	Mintage	Issue Price
M-6	1960	Bronze	59.5mm	115 gm.	10,000	4.50
M-6a	1961	.935 fine silver	35mm	29.5 gm.	5,000	Sold out

OBV: Same as No. M-6, but with English inscription "PRESENTED / BY THE / ISRAEL / GOVERNMENT / TOURIST / CORPORATION" to left.

Edge: Same as No. M-6.

Number	Date	Metal	Diameter	Weight	Mintage	Issue Price
M-6b	1961	.935 fine silver	35mm	30 gm.	5,000	8.00

BAR-KOCHBA MEDAL   M-7

The seventh medal was struck to commemorate the discoveries of the expedition to the Judean Desert Caves. In the Spring of 1960, an archaeological team from the Hebrew University, aided by Israel's Defense Army, explored the rock caves of the Judean Desert. The most important find was a bundle of papyri, enveloping letters of Bar-Kochba, leader of the second Jewish revolt against the Romans (AD 132-135). Mr. David Ben-Gurion, then Prime Minister of Israel, requested that a medal be struck and offered as a souvenir to all who participated in the expedition. Designed by Jacob Zim.

OBV: In the center, an incuse shape suggesting the mouth of a cave, the Judean Hills in the background, a rope ladder in the foreground, and, at the entrance to the cave, the figure of a man hauling up a comrade; above, "SURVEY EXPEDITION TO THE JUDEAN DESERT CAVES IN THE TWELFTH YEAR OF THE STATE OF ISRAEL" in Hebrew; below, "EXPEDITION TO THE JUDEAN DESERT CAVES/1960" in English.

REV: Within an incuse geometrical shape with curved sides, the bundle of papyri, on which writing is legible; below, a coin of Bar-Kochba; on the upper rim, in ancient Hebrew script copied from the letters, "SHIMON BAR-KOCHBA, PRINCE OF ISRAEL"; on the lower left rim, "THE WAR OF BAR-KOCHBA AD 132-135" in Hebrew; on the upper right rim, "BAR KOCHBA WAR AD 132-135" in English followed by "SHIMON PRINCE OF ISRAEL" in Hebrew.

Edge: Incuse, a miniature emblem of the State and "STATE OF ISRAEL" in Hebrew and English.

Number	Date	Metal	Diameter	Weight	Mintage	Issue Price
M-7	1960	Bronze	60mm	116.5 gm.	20,000	4.50
M-7a	1961	.935 fine silver	35mm	29.5 gm.	5,000	8.00
M-7b	1961	.935 fine silver	59.5mm	123.2 gm.	3,000	29.50

INTERNATIONAL CONGRESS OF LOCAL
AUTHORITIES   M-8

The eighth medal was struck to commemorate the Fifteenth Congress of the International Union of Local Authorities (IULA) held in November, 1960, in Tel-Aviv. The Israel Minister of the Interior acted as host. Delegates came from all parts of the world, and in one resolution, called upon the older, richer, and well-established countries to help their newer and needier fellow nations. Designed by Josef Bass.

OBV: In center, on a smooth center panel flanked by half circles of grad-uated ridges, an emblem of the State; inscriptions below, "PRE-SENTED BY THE/MINISTER OF INTERIOR/OF ISRAEL/TO," (blank space), "DELEGATE OF," (blank space), in English. This inscription appeared only on medals presented at the congress; all other medals were left blank below the emblem of the State.

REV: In center panel, the emblem of the congress, a key merging into a Menora with the Roman numeral XV forming the lower part of the key and the word "ISRAEL" in English in a semicircle above the Menora; below this, the inscription "INTERNATIONAL/ CONGRESS OF/LOCAL AUTHORITIES/NOVEMBER/16-23, 1960" in English; all on a raised central panel flanked by half circles bearing the Hebrew inscription "FIFTEENTH CONGRESS OF THE INTERNATIONAL UNION OF LOCAL AUTHORITIES" divided, half to the left and half to the right.

Edge: Incuse, a miniature emblem of the State and "STATE OF ISRAEL" in Hebrew and English.

Number	Date	Metal	Diameter	Weight	Mintage	Issue Price
M-8	1960	Bronze	60mm	117.5 gm.	5,000	4.50
M-8a	1961	.935 fine silver	35mm	29.5 gm.	3,000	8.00

SIXTH PENTECOSTAL WORLD CONFERENCE MEDAL   M-9

The ninth medal was struck to commemorate the Convention of the Pentecostal Fellowship in May, 1961, in Jerusalem. The movement is characterized by a belief in the restoration of New Testament pneumatics (spirituals) in the church, made possible through personal baptisms in the Holy Spirit. Designed by Josef Bass.

OBV: Above, the emblem of the State; below, the inscription "PRESENTED BY THE/GOVERNMENT OF ISRAEL/TO THE MEMBERS OF THE/SIXTH PENTACOSTAL/WORLD CONFERENCE/JERUSALEM, ISRAEL/MAI (*sic.*) 19-21, 1961" in English.

REV: Above, within an incuse semicircle, the emblem of the Pentecostal Fellowship; below, the inscription "FOR OUT OF ZION/SHALL GO THE LAW/AND THE WORD/OF THE LORD FROM/JERUSALEM/ISAIAH 2, 3" in English except for the words ZION and JERUSALEM, which are rendered in Hebrew.

Edge: Incuse, a miniature emblem of the State and "STATE OF ISRAEL" in Hebrew and English.

Number	Date	Metal	Diameter	Weight	Mintage	Issue Price
M-9	1961	Bronze	60mm	120 gm.	5,000	4.50

INTERNATIONAL PRESS INSTITUTE ASSEMBLY
MEDAL   M-10

The tenth medal was struck to commemorate the Tenth General Assembly of the International Press Institute in May, 1961, in Tel-Aviv. The central aim of the IPI is to safeguard the freedom of the press all over the world, to uphold the right of journalists to free access to all sources of news, and to maintain the dignity of the press. Designed by Josef Bass.

OBV: The emblem of the State; below, "PRESENTED/BY THE/GOVERNMENT/OF ISRAEL" in French.

REV: Emblem of the International Press Institute, a globe surmounted by the initials "IPI"; on a raised band transversing the whole width of the medal, "INTERNATIONAL PRESS INSTITUTE" in English; above left, "TENTH/GENERAL/ASSEMBLY" in English; below left, "TEL-AVIV/MAY, 1961" in English and Hebrew.

Edge: Incuse, a miniature emblem of the State and "STATE OF ISRAEL" in Hebrew and English.

Number	Date	Metal	Diameter	Weight	Mintage	Issue Price
M-10	1961	Bronze	60mm	120 gm.	5,000	4.50

BNEI-BERAQ MEDAL   M-11

The eleventh medal was struck by the Municipality of Bnei Beraq, in central Israel, to commemorate the twenty-fifth birthday of the town. In bygone days, Bnei-Beraq was an "academy" of pious learning, and the devout tradition has been revived in modern times by the establishment there of yeshivot (Talmudical colleges) and diverse religious foundations. Designed by Josef Bass.

OBV: In center, on a smooth panel flanked by half circles of graduated ridges, the town's coat of arms, showing the rising sun between two hills and the Tables of the Law dividing, on a ribbon, the phrase "MUNICIPALITY OF BNEI-BERAQ" in Hebrew; above the coat of arms, "MUNICIPALITY OF/BNEI-BERAQ" in Hebrew; below the coat of arms, "MUNICIPALITY/OF/BNEI-BERAQ/ISRAEL" in English.

REV: At upper left, the emblem of the State with "AND JEHUD AND BNEI-BERAQ AND GATH-RIMMON, JOSHUA 19" directly below in Hebrew; to right, a curved olive branch and, outside the branch following the curve of the rim, the inscription from Joshua repeated in English.

Edge: Incuse, a miniature emblem of the State and "STATE OF ISRAEL" in Hebrew and English.

Number	Date	Metal	Diameter	Weight	Mintage	Issue Price
M-11	1961	Bronze	59.5mm	119.3 gm.	5,000	4.50

BAR-MITZVAH MEDAL   M-12

The twelfth medal was struck to commemorate the Thirteenth Anniversary of the Statehood of Israel, or the "Bar-Mitzvah." The Bar-Mitzvah is the age old ceremony which takes place when a boy becomes thirteen or the age of congregational maturity and takes his place beside his father in the Temple. Designed by Rothschild and Lippmann.

OBV: In center, on a shield, the emblem of the State, surrounded by the emblems of the Twelve Tribes of Israel, all on shields pointing inward; around the rim in Hebrew and English, the inscription, "BAR-MITZVAH OF THE STATE OF ISRAEL."

REV: A youth in prayer shawl and phylacteries, reading from the scroll of the Law, with the year 1961 in English and Hebrew on the fringe of the shawl; in the center is the Hebrew inscription; "OF AGE (THIRTEEN YEARS) TO FULFILL THE LAW'S COMMANDMENTS" (Ethics of the Fathers 5:24); around the rim, the English version of the inscription, "AT 13 FOR THE FULLFILLMENT OF THE MITZVOTH P'A-5-24."

Edge: Incuse, a miniature emblem of the State and STATE OF ISRAEL in English and Hebrew. The silver medals are marked by the word "STERLING" in English and by "SILVER .935" in Hebrew. The large silver medals are serially numbered. The edge of the gold medal is milled.

Number	Date	Metal	Diameter	Weight	Mintage	Issue Price
M-12	1961	Bronze	60mm	118 gm.	25,000	4.50
M-12a	1961	.935 fine silver	35.2mm	29.8 gm.	10,000	8.00
M-12b	1961	.935 fine silver	59.5mm	113 gm.	3,000	29.50
M-12c	1961	.935 silver	19mm	7.5 gm.	Unlimited	1.50
M-12d	1961	18 carat gold	27.4mm	14.92 gm.	10,000	43.80
M-12e	1961	18 carat gold	22.3mm	7.97 gm.	20,000	26.25
M-12f	1961	18 carat gold	19.3mm	4.96 gm.	4,000	18.30

NOTE: The miniature (19mm) silver medal also was issued in a key-ring at an issue price of $2.50.

THIRD INTERNATIONAL VIOLONCELLO
COMPETITION   M-13

The thirteenth medal was struck for the Third Pablo Casals International Violoncello Competition held in Jerusalem in 1961. Casals gave a series of concerts while in Israel and presented the awards to the successful contestants. Designed by Josef Bass.

OBV: A cello half hidden by a panel within which is the emblem of the State; inscription around the rim in Hebrew, "THE THIRD PABLO CASALS INTERNATIONAL VIOLONCELLO COMPETITION."

REV: In center, within an incuse square with rounded angles, the head and shoulders of Pablo Casals playing his cello, with an olive branch at the lower right corner; below, the date "1961" in English; inscription around rim in English, "THE THIRD PABLO CASALS INTERNATIONAL VIOLONCELLO COMPETITION."

Edge: Incuse, a miniature emblem of the State and "STATE OF ISRAEL" in Hebrew and English. The silver medals are marked with the word "STERLING" in English and "SILVER .935" in Hebrew. The large silver medals are serially numbered.

Number	Date	Metal	Diameter	Weight	Mintage	Issue Price
M-13	1961	Bronze	59.5mm	113.6 gm.	5,000	4.50
M-13a	1961	.935 fine silver	35mm	30 gm.	5,000	8.00
M-13b	1961	.935 fine silver	59.5mm	110 gm.	3,000	29.50

SECOND INTERNATIONAL BIBLE CONTEST MEDAL   M-14

The fourteenth medal was struck for the Second International Bible Contest in October, 1961, in Jerusalem. This contest has become an integral feature of Israeli life, and excites great interest all over the world among Jews and non-Jews alike. The winner of this occasion was Rabbi Yehye Alshekh of Jerusalem; Madame Yolanda de Silva, a Brazilian housewife, came a very close second. Mr. David Ben-Gurion, Israel's Prime Minister at the time, presented the prizes. The first and second prizes were replicas in gold of the medal itself. Designed by Rothschild and Lippmann.

OBV: Above, the emblem of the State; below to left, one of the ancient Qumran scrolls found in the Judean Desert and, to the right, the jar in which it was found; around the rim, the inscription in Hebrew and French, "SECOND INTERNATIONAL BIBLE CONTEST, JERUSALEM, 1961."

REV: At the bottom, an ancient Jewish lamp; in the center "HOW I LOVED THY LAW" and the source "PSALM 118:97" in Hebrew; around the rim, the same verse and source in the Greek Septuagint version.

Edge: Incuse, a miniature emblem of the State and "STATE OF ISRAEL" in Hebrew and English. The silver medals are marked with the word "STERLING" in English and "SILVER .935" in Hebrew. The large silver medals are serially numbered.

Number	Date	Metal	Diameter	Weight	Mintage	Issue Price
M-14	1961	Bronze	59.5mm	115.5 gm.	10,000	4.50
M-14a	1961	.935 fine silver	35.35mm	29.45 gm.	5,000	8.00
M-14b	1961	.935 fine silver	59.5mm	110.1 gm.	3,000	29.50

SHAVIT MEDAL   M-15

The fifteenth medal was struck in honor of Israel's meterological rocket, "Shavit" (Hebrew for "comet"), launched on August 5, 1961. The rocket was planned and built, and launched, by a team of Israeli scientists. The propellant was an original solid fuel developed in Israel, employing raw materials most of which are locally available. Israel thus became the seventh member of the exclusive meterological club made up of the United States, the Soviet Union, France, Britain, Italy, and Japan. The knowledge acquired by the experiment has been placed at the disposal of scientific institutions in Israel and their counterparts abroad with which Israel is in scientific contact and correspondence. Designed by Miriam Karoli.

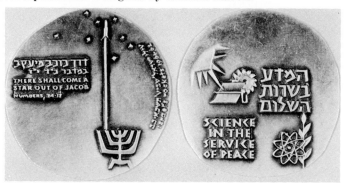

OBV: At right, a seven-branche Menora from which a rocket soars upward to a star-studded sky; to the left, in Hebrew and English, the inscription "THERE SHALL COME A STAR OUT OF JACOB" and the source, "NUMBERS 24:17"; to the right around the rim, "ISRAEL'S ROCKETS 1961-62" in Hebrew and English.

REV: Four square panels, two of them incuse; in the upper right panel, "SCIENCE IN THE SERVICE OF PEACE" in Hebrew; in the lower left panel, the same inscription in English; in the upper left panel, equipment for the application of solar energy; and on the lower right panel, a stylized design of the atom with an olive branch behind.

Edge: Incuse, a miniature emb'em of the State and "STATE OF ISRAEL" in Hebrew and English. Silver medals are marked by the word "STERLING" in English and "SILVER .935" in Hebrew. The large silver medals are serially numbered.

Number	Date	Metal	Diameter	Weight	Mintage	Issue Price
M-15	1962	Bronze	59mm	118 gm.	25,000	4.50
M-15a	1962	.935 fine silver	35mm	30 gm.	5,000	8.00
M-15b	1962	.935 silver	59mm	115 gm.	3,000	29.50

KADMAN NUMISMATIC MUSEUM MEDAL   M-16

The sixteenth medal was struck in bronze on the occasion of the inauguration of the Kadman Numismatic Museum building in October, 1961. The silver medal was struck in commemoration of the opening of the permanent exhibition in April, 1962. This museum is considered one of the world's most outstanding numismatic museums, not only in architectural layout, but in its comprehensive collection of ancient coins, in which it surpasses even the British Museum. Designed by Jacob Zim.

OBV: In an incuse square with rounded corners, the inscription "THE KADMAN/NUMISMATIC/MUSEUM/TEL-AVIV" in Hebrew and English; around the left rim in Hebrew and English, the inscription "INAUGURATION OCTOBER, 1961" on the bronze medals and "DEDICATION APRIL 1962" on the silver medals.

REV: A stylized design of the museum surrounded by three saplings.

Edge: Incuse, a miniature emblem of the State and "STATE OF ISRAEL" in Hebrew and English. The silver medals are marked with the word "STERLING" in English and "SILVER .935" in Hebrew.

Number	Date	Metal	Diameter	Weight	Mintage	Issue Price
M-16	1961	Bronze	60mm	117 gm.	5,000	4.50
M-16a	1962	.935 fine silver	35mm	29.5 gm.	2,000	8.00

WORLD COUNCIL OF SYNAGOGUES MEDAL   M-17

The seventeenth medal was struck to commemorate the First International Congress of the World Council of Synagogues, which was opened in Jerusalem by President Ben-Zvi on May 29, 1962. The objectives of the council are to give guidance to communities, to transmit Judism's precious heritage to future generations, to combat assimilation, and to make the people of Israel a light unto the nations. Designed by Miriam Karoli.

OBV: Within an incuse rectangle set to the left, the Hebrew inscription PRESENTED BY THE PRIME MINISTER'S OFFICE TO THE PARTICIPANTS IN THE CONGRESS OF THE WORLD COUNCIL OF SYNAGOGUES"; outside the rectangle at the upper right corner, the emblem of the State; at the lower right corner, the date "MAY 29-31, 1962" in Hebrew and English.

REV: Within an incuse circle, the emblem of the World Council consisting of stylized rays, in the center of which are the Hebrew words, "LET US WALK IN THE LIGHT OF THE LORD" (Isaiah 11:5); around the rim, the inscription "WORLD COUNCIL OF SYNAGOGUES" above in Hebrew and below in English.

Edge: Incuse, a miniature emblem of the State and "STATE OF ISRAEL" in Hebrew and English.

Number	Date	Metal	Diameter	Weight	Mintage	Issue Price
M-17	1962	Bronze	60mm	118 gm.	5,000	4.50

AMERICAN JEWISH CONGRESS MEDAL   M-18

The eighteenth medal was struck to commemorate the American Jewish Congress Conference held in Israel June 12-14, 1962. There were 500 members present who conducted an American-Israel Dialogue at Binyanei Ha'ooma in Jerusalem. The dialogue was a frank discussion of the problems of the relationship between the Jews of Israel and the Jews of the Diaspora (Jews not living in the national homeland). Designed by Miriam Karoli.

OBV: Within an incuse circle, the emblem of the Israel Government Tourist Corporation, two men carrying a huge cluster of grapes, at right; below and toward the left, "PRESENTED BY THE/ ISRAEL GOVERNMENT/TOURIST CORPORATION" in English; around the circle on the rim, "AMERICAN JEWISH CONGRESS CONFERENCE IN ISRAEL JUNE 1962" in Hebrew.

REV: On a raised semicircular panel to the right, the emblem of the congress, the English letters AJC arranged to form a six-pointed star with a horn above the top point; to the left, the inscriptions "AMERICAN JEWISH/CONGRESS" and "CONFERENCE/IN ISRAEL/JUNE 1962" in English.

Edge: Incuse, a miniature emblem of the State and "STATE OF ISRAEL" in Hebrew and English.

Number	Date	Metal	Diameter	Weight	Mintage	Issue Price
M-18	1962	Bronze	60mm	118 gm.	5,000	4.50

SECOND MUSIC AND DRAMA FESTIVAL IN ISRAEL   M-19

The nineteenth medal was struck to commemorate the Second Festival of Music and Drama, August to September, 1962, in Israel. The Music and Drama Festival has become a permanent feature of the life of Israel. It reflects the resolve to broaden cultural horizons by bringing to Israel some of the world's best musical performances and finest stagecraft. By combining Israeli achievements with international contributions, the event is developing a character all its own which attracts and stimulates both Israelis and visitors. The Israel Government Coins and Medals Corporation struck for the occasion a special medal which was presented to each of the performers, engraved with a personal dedication. Designed by Miriam Karoli

OBV: In the center toward the upper right, the symbol of the festival; below toward the left, "MUSIC AND DRAMA, SECOND FESTIVAL IN ISRAEL, AUGUST-SEPTEMBER, 1962" in Hebrew; around the rim to right and below, the same inscription in English.

REV: Within an incuse circle, four asymmetrical quadrilaterals of varying sizes, on the upper left of which is a harp symbolizing music, on the upper right the emblem of the State, on the lower left the English inscription "PRESENTED/BY THE/PRIME/MINISTER'S/OFFICE," and on the lower right, a Greek mask symbolizing drama.

Edge: Incuse, a miniature emblem of the State and "STATE OF ISRAEL" in Hebrew and English.

Number	Date	Metal	Diameter	Weight	Mintage	Issue Price
M-19	1962	Bronze	60mm	118 gm.	5,000	4.50

SECOND INTERNATIONAL HARP CONTEST MEDAL   M-20

The twentieth medal was struck to commemorate the Second International Harp Contest in September, 1962, in Jerusalem. This contest is planned to take place every three years; the first was in 1959 (see M-5). The prize, a grand concert harp, was awarded in 1962 to a young American girl of 21. All contestants were presented with the medal, a personal dedication engraved on each medal. Designed by Miriam Karoli.

OBV: To the left a stylized harp; to the right, above, the emblem of the State, in the center the inscriptions "SECOND INTERNATIONAL HARP CONTEST JERUSALEM SEPTEMBER 1962" and "PRESENTED BY THE COMMITTEE OF THE ISRAELI HARP FESTIVAL" in French, and below a raised panel for the recipient's name.

REV: Within an irregular incuse shape, the stylized figure of a man in ancient Jewish garb seated with a harp; around rim, "SECOND INTERNATIONAL HARP CONTEST" above and "JERUSALEM SEPTEMBER 1962" below, both in Hebrew.

Edge: Incuse, a miniature emblem of the State and "STATE OF ISRAEL" in Hebrew and English.

Number	Date	Metal	Diameter	Weight	Mintage	Issue Price
M-20	1962	Bronze	60mm	118 gm.	5,000	4.50

MEDAL OF LIBERATION   M-21

The twenty-first medal was struck as a slightly changed replica of the Judaea Capta-Israel Liberata medal (M-1b) issued in 1959. The theme symbolizes the historic turning-point from bondage to freedom by contrasting the Roman motif of "Judaea Capta" with a vista of the new life in independence. Designed by Rothschild and Lippmann.

OBV: In center, within a deep incuse circle, a replica of a Roman "Judaea Capta" coin; around on the rim, a chain broken by "JUDAEA CAPTIVE 3830" in Hebrew above and "JUDAEA CAPTIVE AD 70" in English below. The coin pictures a seven-branched palmtree symbolizing Judaea, the standing emperor to the left, a seated mourning Jewess to the right, "JUDAEA" at left on the rim, "CAPTA" at right on the rim, and SC (for Senatus Consulto, by decree of the Senate) in exergue.

REV: Within a deep incuse circle, a seven-branched palmtree symbolizing Israel; at left a woman joyously holding her child toward the sun; at right a man planting a sapling; on the rim, ISRAEL LIBERATED 5718" in Hebrew above and "ISRAEL LIBERATED 1948" in English below.

Edge: Incuse, a miniature emblem of the State and "STATE OF ISRAEL" in Hebrew and English. The two larger silver medals have the word "STERLING" in English and "SILVER .935" in Hebrew. The large silver medal is serially numbered. The miniature medals have milled edges.

Number	Date	Metal	Diameter	Weight	Mintage	Issue Price
M-21	1962	Bronze	59mm	118 gm.	25,000	4.50
M-21a	1962	.935 fine silver	35mm	20 gm.	10,000	8.00
M-21b	1962	.935 fine silver	59mm	118 gm.	5,000	29.50
M-21c	1962	.935 fine silver	19mm	1.5 gm.	Unlimited	1.50

NOTE: The miniature (19mm) silver medal was also issued in a key-ring at an issue price of $2.50. A Bronze miniature (22mm) exists as part of a plastic bookmark given as a New Year Remembrance by the Israel Government Coins and Medals Corporation in 1965 (see NY-2 in the chapter on New Year Remembrances).

UNITED JEWISH APPEAL 25TH ANNIVERSARY
MEDAL M-22

The twenty-second medal was struck to commemorate the 25th Anniversary of the United Jewish Appeal. The UJA was launched in 1938 at a time when Jewish communities in Europe were facing a frightful threat to their survival. Since then, the Jews of America, the Jewish Agency, and the State of Israel have shared the historic responsibility for the salvation of every Jew unable to live freely in his present country of domicile and for his integration in a recreated homeland. The Appeal now marks with pride its 25th anniversary of rescue and rebuilding. This medal in gold has been presented to leaders of the Appeal in Israel and the U.S.A. Designed by Jacob Zim.

OBV: To upper left, the large numeral "25," in the center of which is the symbol of the UJA; below "YEARS OF/RESCUE/AND/RE-BUILDING" in English; on semicircular raised panel to the right, the emblem of the State and "PRESENTED BY/THE STATE OF/ISRAEL FOR/LEADERSHIP/IN THE/UNITED/JEWISH/APPEAL" in English with the date 1963 in English and Hebrew below.

REV: A view of immigrants disembarking from a ship; in left center, "BRING MY SONS . . . AND DAUGHTERS FROM THE ENDS OF THE EARTH" and the source, "ISAIAH 43:6" both in Hebrew; around the rim below, the same verse in English.

Edge: Incuse, a miniature emblem of the State and "STATE OF ISRAEL" in Hebrew and English. The silver medal has the word "SILVER .935" in Hebrew and "STERLING" in English. The silver medal is serially numbered.

Number	Date	Metal	Diameter	Weight	Mintage	Issue Price
M-22	1962	Bronze	60mm	120 gm.	10,000	4.50
M-22a	1962	.935 fine silver	60mm	115 gm.	3,000	29.50

HEBREW UNION COLLEGE MEDAL   M-23

The twenty-third medal was struck in March of 1963 to signalize the final construction in Jerusalem of the Biblical and Archaeological School, the Hebrew Union College — Jewish Institute of Religion. A meeting of the board of governors was held in the Israel capital and all who attended were presented this medal by the Minister of Education and Culture. Designed by a committee.

OBV: In the center, a raised panel flanked by Arabesque patterns; above, each letter in its own incuse square, the initials of the parent institution, "HUC/JIR" with "MEETING/OF THE BOARD/OF GOVERNORS" and "JERUSALEM/MARCH 24-31 1963" below in English; around on the rim, "HEBREW UNION COLLEGE BIBLICAL AND ARCHAEOLOGICAL SCHOOL" in Hebrew above and English below.

REV: On a central panel flanked by Arabesque patterns, the emblem of the State with "PRESENTED BY/THE MINISTER/OF EDUCATION/TO" with a blank space below.

Edge: Incuse, a miniature emblem of the State and "STATE OF ISRAEL" in Hebrew and English.

Number	Date	Metal	Diameter	Weight	Mintage	Issue Price
M-23	1963	Bronze	60mm	120 gm.	5,000	4.50

THE GHETTO UPRISINGS 20TH ANNIVERSARY
MEDAL   M-24

The twenty-fourth medal was issued to commemorate the 20th anniversary of the Jewish Resistance in the ghetto of Warsaw. On the dark canvas of the holocaust of European Jewry, the heroism of a handful of Warsaw Jews in their long withstanding of Nazi battalions has set an eternal image of resolve and fortitude, of human dignity and self-respect, of utter and final giving of self, so that Israel's name and honor would be upheld. The committee appointed to choose the design selected the work of sculptor Moshe Zipper.

OBV: The figure of a rebel, grenade in hand; behind him, a crumbling wall (the inspiration is a statue of Mordechai Anilewitz, commander of the ghetto uprising, who fell during the battle. The statue is by Nathan Rappaport and stands in the Kibbutz Yad Mordechai in the Negev); around the rim to the right, "THE GHETTO UPRISINGS—20th ANNIVERSARY—1943-1963" in Hebrew and English.

REV: An eternal light (Ner Tamid) from the memorial shrine in Yad Va'Shem, Jerusalem (where the ashes of victims of the death camps are interred. The shrine is called the Hill of Remembrance, and the eternal lights are the work of Elui Kossoy); around the rim to the right, "I WILL GIVE THEM AN EVERLASTING NAME" in Hebrew and English; on the rim to the left, the source "ISAIAH 56:5" in Hebrew and English; at the base of the eternal light is "THE ETERNAL LIGHT ON THE HILL OF REMEMBRANCE" in Hebrew.

Edge: Incuse, a miniature emblem of the State and "STATE OF ISRAEL" in Hebrew and English. The silver medal has the word "STERLING" in English and "SILVER .935" in Hebrew, and is serially numbered.

Number	Date	Metal	Diameter	Weight	Mintage	Issue Price
M-24	1963	Bronze	59mm	120 gm.	50,000	4.50
M-24a	1963	.935 fine silver	59mm	111 gm.	3,000	29.50

TOWER AND STOCKADE MEDAL   M-25

The twenty-fifth medal was struck to commemorate the 25th anniversary of the settlement of Western Galilee. During the years 1936-1939, when the Arabs rioted in Mandatory Palestine, a daring form of Jewish settlement was undertaken in the remotest corners of the country. New farmsteads were established, completely defended by the watchtower and stockade. The settlement of Western Galilee began in March, 1938, and the settlements so established were the only outposts in the outbreak of the war of independence. The settlements were Hanita, on a lofty and lonely wooded hill on the Lebanese border, Eylon, Matzuba, and Nahariya on the seashore. Obverse designed by Rothschild and Lippmann; reverse designed by Gabriel Neuman.

OBV: Divided into three sections; on the left, "25TH ANNIVERSARY OF THE CONQUEST OF WESTERN GALILEE" in Hebrew; above right, the emblem of the Regional Council; lower right, a schematic map of Western Galilee, with the three villages of "HANITA," "EYLON," and "MATZPBA" marked by their names and towers; a pattern of sea waves is seen on the west, and the Lebanese border is marked just north of Hanita.

REV: The verse from II Chronicles 14:6, "LET US MAKE ABOUT THEM WALLS AND TOWERS" in Hebrew, one word enlarged to form the stylized outline of a tower and stockade foundation; below is the source of the verse in Hebrew and the dates 1938-1963 in Hebrew and English; around the rim is the verse repeated in English, with the source to the left of the tower.

Edge: Incuse, a miniature emblem of the State and "STATE OF ISRAEL" in Hebrew and English.

Number	Date	Metal	Diameter	Weight	Mintage	Issue Price
M-25	1963	Bronze	59mm	114 gm.	5,000	4.50

ISRAEL ARMED FORCES REMEMBRANCE DAY MEDAL

On the eve of the fifteenth anniversary of Israel's independence, this medal was presented to the kin of the fallen soldiers by the responsible unit of the Ministry of Defense. It contrasts on its two sides the destruction wrought by Rome to Judaea in AD 70 and the independence now restored by the supreme sacrifice of Jewish fighters for freedom. This medal is for presentation purposes only, and is not for sale. Collectors are asked to refrain from tactless requests to purchase this medal; for this reason, it has not been assigned a catalog number.

OBV: Divided vertically into two equal sections, the right one incuse; vertically in center to right of the dividing line, a stylized olive branch symbolizing peace; to the right above, within a rectangle with rounded angles, the palmtree symbolizing Israel with a Jewess lifting her child toward the sun and a man planting a sapling (this design is derived from the Medal of Liberation, M-1 and M-21); below, following the rim, ISRAEL LIBERATED; to the left of the dividing line, "TO THE MEMORY OF THOSE WHO FELL FOR ITS INDEPENDENCE" and "MINISTRY OF DEFENSE." All inscriptions in Hebrew.

REV: Two equal sections divided vertically, the right one incuse; vertically to the right of the dividing line, a chain symbolizing the Roman subjugation; to the right above, a reproduction of a 'Judaea Capta" coin as depicted on the Medal of Liberation; below, following the rim, "JUDAEA CAPTIVE 3830"; to the left of the dividing line, REMEMBRANCE DAY FOR THE FALLEN OF THE ISRAEL DEFENSE ARMY, 5723." All inscriptions in Hebrew.

Edge: Incuse, a miniature emblem of the State and "STATE OF ISRAEL" in Hebrew and English, plus the inscription, "MANPOWER DEPARTMENT, DIVISION FOR THE COMMEMORATION OF THE FALLEN" in Hebrew.

Date	Metal	Diameter	Weight	
1963	Bronze	60mm	120 gm.	**NOT FOR SALE**

Z.O.A. CONVENTION MEDAL   M-26

The twenty-sixth medal was struck to commemorate the 66th convention of the Zionist Organization of America, the first ever held in Israel. It was held in Jerusalem July 11-17, 1963, and coincided with the tenth anniversary of the ZOA House in Tel-Aviv, where its working sessions took place. The late President John F. Kennedy had cabled, "The integrity and security of Israel is a matter with which we can properly concern ourselves." Designed by Jacob Zim.

OBV: Upper right, on a raised panel, the emblem of the State; below and to the left, the inscription "PRESENTED/BY THE/GOVERNMENT OF ISRAEL" in English on raised panels.

REV: Upper left, two interlinked raised panels, on the upper the emblem of the ZOA, on the lower the Star of David; below on a raised rectangle, "THE 66TH/Z.O.A./CONVENTION/JULY 11-17 1963/ FIRST IN ISRAEL" in English; to the right on another raised rectangle, the same inscription in Hebrew.

Edge: Incuse, a miniature emblem of the State and "STATE OF ISRAEL" in Hebrew and English.

Number	Date	Metal	Diameter	Weight	Mintage	Issue Price
M-26	1963	Bronze	60mm	107 gm.	5,000	4.50

THE ISRAEL FESTIVAL MEDAL   M-27

The twenty-seventh medal was struck to commemorate the third Israel Festival in Jerusalem, July 16, 1963. Distinguished artists from many countries interpreted masterpieces of world art in music and related fields. Biblical themes by great composers, Jewish liturgical music, and synagogue chants figures prominently in the program. Designed by Miriam Karoli.

OBV: At upper left, the emblem of the State; in the center, "THE ISRAEL FESTIVAL 5723" in Hebrew merging into the emblem of the festival on the right; below, "THE ISRAEL FESTIVAL 1963" in English. The obverse is concave.

REV: Three incuse irregular squares arranged vertically, in the top square a stringed instrument representing music, in the middle a mask representing drama, and in the bottom square a pair of ballet slippers representing dance; to the left in an incuse rectangle, PRESENTED BY THE/PRIME MINISTER'S/OFFICE" in English. The reverse is convex.

Edge: Incuse, a miniature emblem of the State and "STATE OF ISRAEL" in Hebrew and English.

Number	Date	Metal	Diameter	Weight	Mintage	Issue Price
M-27	1963	Bronze	60mm	113 gm.	5,000	4.50

FIRST SETTLERS YEAR MEDAL   M-28

The twenty-eighth medal was struck to commemorate the "First Settlers Year". It inaugurated a year long educational program to honor the first pioneers and to clarify the roots of their settlement in Israel. The official definition of the First Settlers Year was the 80th Anniversary of the Bilu immigration and the first colonies, but this is not historically accurate, nor was it intended to be, since the settlement of Petach Tikva was founded 85 years before and before that there had been at least two experiments in colonization in Galilee. For this reason, the First Settlers Year was officially concluded in Petach Tikva, mother of the colonies. The obverse was designed by Gabriel Neuman, the reverse by Josef Bass.

OBV: To the right, the emblem of the state; to the left along the rim, "ISRAEL IN HOMAGE TO THE FIRST ONES" in English; in the center, the same inscription in large incuse Hebrew letters.

REV: A man planting in a swamp with a stockade and buildings in the background; around the rim to the left, "I WILL REMEMBER THE COVENANT OF THEIR ANCESTORS" and the source, "LEVITICUS 26:45" in English; to the right, the same verse and its source in Hebrew.

Edge: Incuse, a miniature emblem of the State and "STATE OF ISRAEL" in Hebrew and English. The silver medals have the word "STERLING" in English and "SILVER .935" in Hebrew and are serially numbered.

Number	Date	Metal	Diameter	Weight	Mintage	Issue Price
M-28	1963	Bronze	59mm	120 gm.	15,000	4.50
M-28a	1963	.935 Fine Silver	59mm	115 gm.	3,000	29.50

TERRA SANCTA MEDAL   M-29

The twenty-ninth medal was specifically designed for pilgrims and visitors to the Holy Land (Terra Sancta.) The verse from Leviticus, "Love thy neighbor as thyself," was selected for the theme by Miriam Karoli, the designer. Arranging the inscriptions in a composition which strikes a medieval note, she followed through with a map in the medieval concept of cartography for the obverse, a map which looks pictorially naive, in particular in its representation of the Holy Land. Designed by Miriam Karoli.

OBV: A relief of the Holy Land in perspective, in the style of ancient maps, with the Mediterranean at the bottom; above center, the Latin inscription "TERRA SANCTA" set between the Sea of Galilee and the Dead Sea.

REV: Above, following the rim, "LOVE THY NEIGHBOR AS THYSELF" in Hebrew; below on the rim, the source "LEVITICUS 19, 18" in English to the left and Hebrew to the right; in the center, the verse repeated in French above and English below.

Edge: Incuse, a miniature emblem of the State and "STATE OF ISRAEL" in Hebrew and English. The silver medals have the word "STERLING" in English and "SILVER .935" in Hebrew. The large medals are serially numbered.

Number	Date	Metal	Diameter	Weight	Mintage	Issue Price
M-29	1963	Bronze	59mm	120 gm.	25,000	4.50
M-29a	1963	.935 fine silver	35mm	30 gm.	15,000	8.00
M-29b	1963	.935 fine silver	59mm	115 gm.	5,000	29.50
M-29c	1963	22 carat gold	35mm	29 gm.	5,000	90.00

S.S. SHALOM MEDAL   M-30

The thirtieth medal was struck in honor of the s.s. Shalom, the flagship of Zim, the Israel Navigation Company. The liner of 24,500 tons was built at the shipyard of St. Nazaire in France. It provides regular service between Israel and the United States, touching at a number of European ports. King Solomon's era of peerless tranquility and well-being was evoked to express the significance of this "Ship of Peace." That was an era of "ships of Tarshish" sailing home with the costliest of wares from faraway lands. And so, ancient and modern are featured in the relief of a beautiful vessel — one of today, and one of Solomon's time — on both obverse and reverse. Designed by Dodo Shenhav, a sculptor of Jerusalem.

OBV: Across an eight-spoked steering wheel, the s.s. Shalom in relief; at upper left in an incuse rectangle, the seven stars of Zim's emblem; below along the rim, between the four bottom spokes, the inscription, "s.s. SHALOM 1964" in English and Hebrew.

REV: In the center, within a wheel rim, a Solomonic "ship of Tarshish" after a model in the Haifa Maritime Museum; below, in Hebrew, KING SOLOMON MADE A NAVY OF SHIPS" and the source "I KINGS 9, 26"; below on the rim, the same verse in English.

Edge: Incuse, a miniature emblem of the State and "STATE OF ISRAEL" in Hebrew and English. The silver medals have the word "STERLING" in English and "SILVER .935" in Hebrew. The large silver medals are serially numbered.

Number	Date	Metal	Diameter	Weight	Mintage	Issue Price
M-30	1964	Bronze	59mm	140 gm.	15,000	4.50
M-30a	1964	.935 fine silver	35mm	30 gm.	5,000	8.00
M-30b	1964	.935 fine silver	59mm	117 gm.	3,000	29.50

FIRST IMMIGRANT BLOCKADE RUNNERS MEDAL   M-31

The thirty-first medal was struck to commemorate the 30th anniversary of the first immigrant blockade runners in Israel. Thirty years ago, the first rescue ship put ashore the first immigrants to be labeled "maapilim" (men and women of daring) by the Yishuv. "Aliya B" was the cover name for the immigration activities, and a committee of personalities who had been active in Aliya B helped determine the design of this medal. Obverse designed by Yizhak Pugacz, reverse by Dodo Shenhav; both designers were "maapilim" themselves.

OBV: A depiction of the Mediterranean and Black Sea in deep incuse with the routes of the blockade runners converging on the Israeli coast; incuse, the dates "1934-1964" in Hebrew above, in English below; around the rim, "30TH ANNIVERSARY OF FIRST IMMIGRANT RUNNERS" in Hebrew above, in English below.

REV: An enlarged barbed wire fence above the relief outline of the Palestine coast; bursting through the fence is a "blockade runner" full of immigrants, heading straight into the beach, where a welcoming group awaits them with upraised arms; below the line of the line of the Jordan River is the inscription "YE DARED TO GO UP" and its source, "DEUT. 1, 41" in Hebrew and English.

Edge: Incuse, a miniature emblem of the State and "STATE OF ISRAEL" in Hebrew and English. The silver medals have the word "STERLING" in English and "SILVER .935" in Hebrew. All medals are serially numbered.

Number	Date	Metal	Diameter	Weight	Mintage	Issue Price
M-31	1964	Bronze	59mm	110 gm.	30,000	4.50
M-31a	1964	.935 fine silver	35mm	30 gm.	5,000	8.00
M-31b	1964	.935 fine silver	59mm	117 gm.	3,000	29.50

"HISTADRUT" MEDAL   M-32

The thirty-second medal was struck in honor of the 14th Congress of the International Federation of Commercial, Clerical, and Technical Employees (IFCCTE), held in Tel-Aviv in May, 1964, and hosted by "Histadrut," the Israeli assembly of trade unions. Designed by the brothers Gabriel and Maxim Shamir.

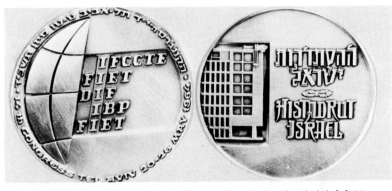

OBV: A sector of the globe to the left; to the right the initial letters of the Congress in capitals; around the rim, "14TH CONGRESS TEL-AVIV 20-26 MAY 1964" in Hebrew and English.

REV: To the left, a schematic design of the Histadrut building in Tel-Aviv; to the right, "HISTADRUT ISRAEL" in Hebrew and English.

Edge: Incuse, a miniature emblem of the State and "STATE OF ISRAEL" in Hebrew and English.

Number	Date	Metal	Diameter	Weight	Mintage	Issue Price
M-32	1964	Bronze	59mm	120 gm.	5,000	4.50

TEL-AVIV INTERNATIONAL TRADE FAIR MEDAL   M-33

The thirty-third medal was struck to honor the opening of the Tel-Aviv International Trade Fair in the summer of 1964. Since the early 1930's, Tel-Aviv, the first Jewish city of modern Israel, has played host to a succession of international trade fairs. Tel-Aviv has developed rapidly into a creative and dynamic center of the arts, industry, and commerce. The geographical position of Israel and the rapid expansion of Tel-Aviv combine to make this occasion a convenient and advantageous meeting place for overseas businessmen and manufacturers. The familiar Flying Camel emblem of the fair has become a universally inviting symbol. Designed by Dodo Shenhav.

OBV: In the center, an ellipse with a map of the world, on which all roads lead to Israel; around the map, the inscription "TEL-AVIV INTERNATIONAL TRADE FAIR 1964" in Hebrew above, in English below; all superimposed on an engraved design of the city of Tel-Aviv.

REV: The Flying Camel in relief against a background of motifs, all incuse, symbolizing agriculture, industry, and commerce, keystones of the achievements which the fair displays.

Edge: Incuse, a miniature emblem of the State and "STATE OF ISRAEL" in Hebrew and English.

Number	Date	Metal	Diameter	Weight	Mintage	Issue Price
M-33	1964	Bronze	59mm	110 gm.	5,000	4.50

SIXTEENTH CHESS OLYMPICS MEDAL   M-34

The thirty-fourth medal was struck to honor the 16th Chess Olympics in Israel in November, 1964. The tournament is held every second year in a different country. The International Chess Federation was established in Paris in 1924 and celebrated its 40th anniversary in Israel. The Israel Chess Association, founded in Jerusalem in 1920, now embraces 150 clubs and over ten thousand players. The obverse was designed by Z. Segal, the reverse by the brothers Gabriel and Maxim Shamir.

OBV: In the center, the emblem of the International Chess Federation, a globe with the Latin inscription "GENS UNA SUMUS" (We are all of one kind) in a central panel; superimposed on the globe is the phrase "ISRAEL 1964" in Hebrew above and English below the panel; around the rim is "16TH CHESS OLYMPICS" in Hebrew above and French below.

REV: A stylized composition of chess pieces.

Edge: Incuse, a miniature emblem of the State and "STATE OF ISRAEL" in Hebrew and English.

Number	Date	Metal	Diameter	Weight	Mintage	Issue Price
M-34	1964	Bronze	59mm	120 gm.	5,000	4.50

MASADA MEDAL   M-35

In the Judaean Hills, high above the western shore of the Dead Sea, rises the flat-topped rock of Masada. It was here the Jews took their final stand against the Romans in the first revolt, AD 66-70. Almost two thousand years later, the archaeologists of Israel are exploring the site, unearthing Herodian palaces, storerooms, baths, reservoirs, thousands of ancient coins, and precious fragments of scrolls. The thirty-fifth medal was struck to mark the excavations of Masada, and all proceeds from the sale of the medal are devoted to the restoration of this important archaeological site. Obverse designed by Nathan Karp, reverse by the brothers Gabriel and Maxim Shamir.

OBV: In the center, a circular composition of Hebrew letters which spell out "MASADA SHALL NOT FALL AGAIN," surrounded by the same phrase in English; around the outside, in a continuous circular design, figures which represent the builders, diggers, and warriors of modern Israel, their weapons and tools a sign of the pledge expressed on the medal.

REV: The Rock of Masada in relief; above, "WE SHALL REMAIN FREE MEN" in Hebrew, below along the rim in English. The remnants of the camps of the besieging legions of Rome are visible at the base of the rock.

Edge: Incuse, a miniature emblem of the State and "STATE OF ISRAEL" in Hebrew and English. The silver medals have the word "STERLING" in English and "SILVER .935" in Hebrew. All medals are serially numbered.

Number	Date	Metal	Diameter	Weight	Mintage	Issue Price
M-35	1964	Bronze	59mm	120 gm.	15,000	4.50
M-35a	1964	.935 fine silver	35mm	30 gm.	5,000	8.00
M-35b	1965	22 carat gold	27mm	15 gm.	3,000	—

THIRD INTERNATIONAL BIBLE CONTEST MEDAL   M-36

The thirty-sixth medal was struck to commemorate the Third International Bible Contest, held in Jerusalem in 1964. These contests have become an integral feature in Israeli life, and excite great interest. The first and second prizes are replicas in gold and silver of this medal. Designed by Rothschild and Lippmann.

OBV: In the center, a crown fabricated from the three Hebrew letters that spell out "TANAK," an acrostic of "Torah" (the Law), "Neviim" (Prophets), and "Ketubim" (Writings) which is the accepted expression for the Old Testament; below is the emblem of the State, and around the rim is "THIRD INTERNATIONAL BIBLE CONTEST JERUSALEM 1964" in Hebrew and French.

REV: Identical to the Second International Bible Contest medal (M-14), an ancient Jewish lamp with "HOW I LOVED THY LAW" and "PSALM 118:97" in Hebrew and Greek Septuagint version.

Edge: Incuse, a miniature emblem of the State and "STATE OF ISRAEL" in Hebrew and English.

Number	Date	Metal	Diameter	Weight	Mintage	Issue Price
M-36	1964	Bronze	55mm	115 gm.	5,000	4.50

ISRAEL MUSEUM MEDAL   M-37

The thirty-seventh medal was struck for the inauguration of the Israel Museum in Jerusalem on May 11, 1965. The buildings are set on a hill in the manner of traditional Mediterranean architecture. The complex comprises the Bezalel Museum of Fine Arts, the Samuel Bronfman Biblical and Archaeological Museum, the Shrine of the Book (housing the Dead Sea scrolls), and the terraced Billy Rose Garden of Art. The theme of the inaugural exhibition was "Biblical Art and Archaeology, for the Bible lives everywhere, but resides here." Designed by Miriam and Mordechai Gumpel.

OBV: Around the rim, a stylized design of the museum buildings, circular to fit the roundness of the medal; in the center, the inscription "THE ISRAEL MUSEUM" in Hebrew, English, and French.

REV: A realistic representation of a stone relief seven-branched candelabra found in a second-century AD synagogue in Tiberias. The branches are composed of conventional pomegranates linked by a horizontal band where recesses for the oil are clearly visible. The original is a rare example of an early Menora which was once in use, as evidenced by the blackening of the little cavities that held the oil for the flame.

Edge: Incuse, a miniature emblem of the State and "STATE OF ISRAEL" in Hebrew and English. The silver medals have the word "STERLING" in English and "SILVER .935" in Hebrew.

Number	Date	Metal	Diameter	Weight	Mintage	Issue Price
M-37	1965	Bronze	45mm	40 gm.	15,000	4.00
M-37a	1965	.935 fine silver	45mm	48 gm.	10,000	14.00

HISTORICAL CITIES IN ISRAEL

Nine medals have been struck featuring nine old-new cities. The obverse of each coin-medal (the official designation of the pieces because each portrays an ancient coin on its reverse) portrays the city as it is today. The artists have sought to give a stylized impression of the city which each medal names, and where, most often, relics of a bygone day still dominate the landscape in spite of rapid contemporary development.

The reverse of each medal pictures an ancient coin connected with the site. The ancient coin chosen as a model for the replica on each of the medals was minted on the very site of the city honored, and testifies pre-eminently to the exceptional character of that city. The coins portrayed bear the names and sometimes the dates of striking in the city. The series is limited to nine cities because coins were struck in only nine locations in ancient Israel.

The value of coins as a historical source lies essentially in their widespread use in early days for purposes other than trade. Coins played a more significant part in early life than they do today, when bills, banknotes, checks, promises, and credit cards all serve as money. The ancients insisted on gold, silver, or bronze for more than 99 per cent of their dealings. Coins also served, just as they do today, as a means of communicating facts, or commemorating victories, or marking the beginning or end of a rule. Coins also provide almost the only evidence of life in some parts of the Holy Land during the second and third centuries.

This series of city medals was issued to give a hint of the rich past and history of Israel. An extensive search for the ideal representative coin of each city chosen meant sifting through thousands of ancient coins to select the best specimen.

Only two of the nine coin-medals reproduce Hebrew coins: the Jerusalem coin, minted by Simon Bar-Kochba in AD 133, and the Caesarea coin, a coin of Agrippa the First bearing that city's name.

The ancient city coin that served as the model for a particular medal is shown in this catalog along with its medallic replica. The medals were designed by three artists new to the art of medal making, who found the series a fresh challenge to their talents.

Mordechai Gumpel and his wife Miriam specialize in murals, mosaic floors, and sculpture. They have created a floor for the Paris headquarters of the International Railways Union, a wall for a London bank, and the gigantic pattern on the wall of the Dagon Silo in Haifa Port.

Jean David came to Israel in 1942 as an illegal immigrant. His posters have won awards in Tokyo, Tangier, and Milan. His oil paintings have been exhibited in several world capitals. Decorations by David, in various media, grace all seven Zim ocean liners and the El Al Airline bureaus in New York and Rome.

Alex Berlyne is a graphic artist who has specialized in editorial art, cover designs, layout, illustrations, and typography. He designed the reverses of all nine medals, as well as the obverses of the Ashkelon and Lod medals.

The medals were struck by a Jerusalem family firm established in 1933, Mr. Shlomo Kretschmer and his two sons, Eliyahu and Aviezer. This firm has struck nearly all of the medals issued by the Israel Government Coins and Medals Corporation since the first one in 1958.

All of the coin-medals are serially numbered.

ASHKELON COIN-MEDAL   M-38

Ashkelon, one of the five city-states of the Philistines, who settled on the seaboard of Canaan in or about the twelfth century BC, was a port of renown in antiquity. It was the birthplace of Herod the Great. In the ruins of old Ashkelon are to be found Hellenistic marbles, a Roman tomb, and a Crusader battlement. Today's Ashkelon is a popular vacationing resort with a swiftly developing industry. Designed by Alex Berlyne.

OBV: A corner of Ashkelon, where a Corinthian capital stands near public buildings of the twentieth century; on the rim, "ASHKELON" in Hebrew above, in English below.

REV: In the center, a replica of an ancient bronze coin of Ashkelon; on the rim, "ASHKELON COIN 47 BC" in Hebrew above and English below. The coin depicts the prow of an oared galley with the Greek abbreviation for "Ashkelon" above and the letters N Z indicating the year 47 BC.

Edge: Incuse, a miniature emblem of the State and "STATE OF ISRAEL" in English and Hebrew. Silver medals have "STERLING .935" on the edge. All medals are serially numbered.

Number	Date	Metal	Diameter	Weight	Mintage	Issue Price
M-38	1965	Bronze	45mm	40 gm.	15,000	4.00
M-38a	1965	.935 fine silver	45mm	48 gm.	10,000	14.00

Issued January 15, 1965.

ACRE COIN-MEDAL   M-39

Acre (Akko) forms the northern tip of the Bay of Haifa, the largest and most spectacular of Israel's Mediterranean coastline. It is among the oldest cities in the world, with an unbroken history of assaults and sieges going back almost four thousand years. Today it is a lively fishing anchorage and a training base for naval officers. Continuing excavation and restoration add to this treasure of history each day. Obverse designed by Mordechai Gumpel, reverse by Alex Berlyne.

OBV: A stylized impression of the city, with a fortress overlooking the sea, a minaret, a cupola, and a palmtree; at the upper left, as though sailing straight out of the past, a Hebrew galleon as pictured in the catacombs of Beit She'arim; on the rim, "ACRE" in Hebrew above left, in English below right.

REV: In the center, a replica of an ancient coin of Acre; on the rim, "COIN OF ACRE AD 217-222" in Hebrew above, in English below. The coin was struck by the Emperor Elagabalus (AD 217-222) and shows the entrance to the port with waves breaking against the mooring arches, a seaboard shrine, and a temple that once stood on the acropolis, in the center of which stands Tyche (Fortune) being garlanded by Nike (Victory); to the left in the temple is Perseus holding the head of Medusa, and to the right stands Athena.

Edge: Same as M-38.

Number	Date	Metal	Diameter	Weight	Mintage	Issue Price
M-39	1965	Bronze	45mm	40 gm.	15,000	4.00
M-39a	1965	.935 fine silver	45mm	48 gm.	10,000	14.00

Issued March 1, 1965.

TIBERIAS COIN-MEDAL   M-40

Tiberias stands midway along the western shore of the Sea of Galilee. It was founded in AD 20 by Herod Antipas in honor of the Roman Emperor Tiberius. After the destruction of the Temple in AD 70 Tiberias became a center of continuing Jewish activity. Lying two hundred meters below sea level, Tiberias has become famous as a spa all down through the ages. Today the tropical climate, the modern hotels, aquatic sports, fishing and sailing, the archaeology, and the kibbutzim that dot the countryside attract visitors all the year around. The obverse was designed by Mordechai Gumpel, the reverse by Alex Berlyne.

OBV: A representation of all that is timeless in Tiberias: the fisherman, a girl with a basket of fruit, an ancient building, and a ship, all against the landscape of the Sea of Galilee and surrounding hills; following the rim, "TIBERIAS" in Hebrew above and English below.

REV: In the center, a replica of an ancient coin of Tiberias; on the rim, "COIN OF TIBERIAS AD 101" in Hebrew above and English below. The coin was minted in AD 101 during the reign of Trajan; it depicts Hygeia, goddess of health, holding a bowl and serpent, seated upon a rock from which the hot springs flow; around Hygeia is the legend "TIBER KLAV" (for Tiberia Klaudia) and in the field are characters indicating "Year 81" of the foundation of the city, corresponding to AD 101.

Edge: Same as M-38.

Number	Date	Metal	Diameter	Weight	Mintage	Issue Price
M-49	1965	Bronze	45mm	40 gm.	15,000	4.00
M-40a	1965	.935 fine silver	45mm	48 gm.	10,000	14.00

Issued April 15, 1965.

BEIT SHE'AN COIN-MEDAL   M-41

Beit She'an stands in a subtropical valley, astride the caravan routes which linked Egypt and Mesopotamia in ancient times. Traces of settlement in Beit She'an go back six thousand years. The earliest records appear in Egyptian texts of the 19th century BC. The site is dominated by a tel (mound) which has been formed by successive layers of city after city, each with its citadel, on the site. Recently a magnificent and well-preserved ampitheatre was uncovered, and a fourth century synagogue with beautiful mosaics featuring, among other motifs, the seven-branched candelabra (Menora). Beit She'an is often mentioned in the Bible. During the Hellenistic period it was named Scythopolis. After the Moslem invasion it sank in importance. Only now has it begun to revive, mainly as an agricultural center. Obverse designed by Mordechai Gumpel, reverse by Alex Berlyne.

OBV: A depiction of the main historical features today: the tel, the Roman theatre, the synagogue mosaic of the seven-branched candelabra, and an Ionic column; along the rim, "BEIT SHE'AN" in Hebrew to upper left, in English to lower right.

REV: In the center, a replica of an ancient coin of Beit She'an; on the rim, "COIN OF BEIT SHE'AN AD 189" in Hebrew above, in English below. The coin was minted during the reign of Emperor Commodus (AD 180-192) and depicts Dionysus, a divinity associated with Beit She'an through his foster mother Nysa (the Roman called the city Nysa-Scythopolis); at his feet lies the sacred panther and around is the inscription "NY.CK.IE.ACY.SMC." standing for the name of the city and year of issue.

Edge: Same as M-38.

Number	Date	Metal	Diameter	Weight	Mintage	Issue Price
M-41	1965	Bronze	45mm	40 gm.	15,000	4.00
M-41a	1965	.935 fine silver	45mm	48 gm.	10,000	14.00

Issued June 1, 1965.

AVDAT COIN-MEDAL   M-42

In the heart of the Negev stands the ruins of the ancient city of Avdat, originally a staging post established by the Nebataeans around the third century BC. They developed a brilliant civilization, combining commerce and agriculture. The town was annexed to the Roman Empire in AD 106. Dating from the Byzantine period are the fortress, the churches, the monastery, the bathhouse, and a whole town of cave dwellings. Even before the Arab conquest, Avdat had suffered a Persian raid, and by the middle of the seventh century AD it lay in ruins. Obverse designed by Mordechai Gumpel, reverse by Alex Berlyne.

OBV: To the right, the arch which served as the entrance to the Avdat acropolis during the historical periods; in center, columns of different sizes; to left, an engraved motif of leaves and branches taken from a Nabataean bowl; below left, a replica of a Roman period stone relief bird; above, the name "AVDAT" in Hebrew, and below in English.

REV: In the center, a replica of an ancient coin of Avdat; on the rim, "NABATAEAN COIN AD 9-40" in Hebrew above and English below. The coin was minted by Nabataean King Aretas IV of the period indicated; in the center of the coin is a double cornucopia crossed at the base; between the horns, an Aramaic inscription meaning "Aretas, Shakilat," the king and his consort.

Edge: Same as M-38.

Number	Date	Metal	Diameter	Weight	Mintage	Issue Price
M-42	1965	Bronze	45mm	40 gm.	15,000	4.00
M-42a	1965	.935 fine silver	45mm	48 gm.	10,000	14.00

Issued July 15, 1965.

CAESAREA COIN-MEDAL   M-43

Between Tel-Aviv and Haifa is Caesarea, rich in archaeology and golden with prospects of development to come. It owes its fame to Herod the Great, who settled in the city by the sea, then called Strato's Tower. The city held a temple to Caesar, a theatre, an ampitheatre, a hippodrome, a marketplace, and many palaces. The Roman procurators of Judaea chose to live there. The Jews resettled there and vestiges of their synagogues are being brought to light today. The city became a center of Christian erudition as well, and its scribes of Holy Writ were especially renowned. The Arabs conquered it in AD 639; then came the Crusaders and eventual Moslem victory. Modern Caesarea appeals to tourists; its golf links, its sea front, and its festival concerts make it a delight to visit. Archaeologists still are unearthing Caesarea's brilliant past. Obverse designed by Mordechai Gumpel, reverse by Alex Berlyne.

OBV: A stylized impression of the city showing a Roman arch with the sea beyond, and below a seven-branched candelabra between acanthus leaves, from a fifth century synagogue in Caesarea; on the rim, "CAESAREA" in Hebrew above and English below.

REV: In the center, a replica of an ancient coin of Caesarea; on the rim, "COIN OF CAESAREA AD 44" in Hebrew above and English below. The coin was minted in Caesarea by Agrippa I (AD 33-47); in the center is a standing figure of Tyche (Fortune), holding in her right hand a ship's rudder, and in her left a palm branch; around is the Greek inscription "CAESAREA, CLOSE TO THE HARBOR SEBASTOS" (Sebastos being Greek for Augustus, for it was to honor him that the city was built); to right in the field, the letters "L H" indicating the year AD 44.

Edge: Same as M-38.

Number	Date	Metal	Diameter	Weight	Mintage	Issue Price
M-43	1965	Bronze	45mm	40 gm.	15,000	4.00
M-43a	1965	.935 fine silver	45mm	48 gm.	10,000	14.00

Issued September 1, 1965.

JAFFA COIN-MEDAL   M-44

Jaffa, which in Hebrew is Yafo, meaning beautiful, is a city with a recorded history of three thousand five hundred years, a city of biblical and mythological legends. The tale of Jonah and the whale is well known: bidden by the Lord to go to Ninevah and pronounce its doom for its wickedness, Jonah sought to escape the divine mission, so he went to Yafo and took a ship to Tashish, but ended up in the belly of a whale for three days. When he was belched forth, he at last was willing to obey the Lord's command. In history there is hardly a conqueror of the land who overlooked this important harbor. Sennacherib took it in 701 BC, Alexander the Great in 332 BC, Honathan the Hasmonean in 148 BC, the Romans destroyed it in AD 68, the Moslems captured it some six centuries later, the Crusaders lost it in 1268, and Napolean seized it in 1799. The first Zionist leaders entered the Promised Land through Jaffa and in 1909 founded Tel-Aviv on its northern dunes. After the re-establishment of Israel in 1948, the two cities became one, and Tel-Aviv-Yafo is its name. Obverse designed by Jean David, reverse by Alex Berlyne.

A. M-44

OBV: In the center, the promontory of Jaffa in the form of Jonah's whale, carrying old-fashioned dwellings on its back; the tail is shaped into three Hebrew letters spelling "YAFO"; above, the name JAFFA in English.

REV: In the center, a replica of an ancient coin of Jaffa; on the rim, "COIN OF JAFFA AD 217-222" above in Hebrew, below in English; the coin bears a standing figure of helmeted Athena resting a shield on one foot, her right hand holding a lance; around is the inscription in Greek, "FLAVIA IOPPE," as Jaffa was called in Hellenistic times (Athena was the goddess of war and reason, and the patron deity of Athens); the coin was minted during the reign of Emperor Elagabalus (AD 217-222).

Edge: Same as M-38.

Number	Date	Metal	Diameter	Weight	Mintage	Issue Price
M-44	1965	Bronze	45mm	40 gm.	15,000	4.00
M-44a	1965	.935 fine silver	45mm	48 gm.	10,000	14.00

Issued October 15, 1965.

LOD COIN-MEDAL   M-45

The Old Testament tells that Shamer, an offspring of Benjamin, built "Lod, with the towns thereof." The town was of modest importance until the destruction of Jerusalem in AD 70. Lod then became the haven of prominent Jewish sages, and for nearly three hundred years it was the center of Jewish learning. Under Roman rule Lod grew in stature and dimension. It was renamed Diospolis—city of Zeus—but the citizens used the name Lod or the Greek form Lydda. Few archaeological relics and historical sites are found in Lod apart from interesting vestiges of the Crusader period. One of Israel's largest airports is located at Lod. Designed by Alex Berlyne.

OBV: The front view of an airplane; underneath an incuse outline of Lod, its Mediterranean features stressed, and a high relief outline of the airport buildings; above right along the rim, "LOD" in English and Hebrew.

REV: In the center, a replica of an ancient coin of Lod; on the rim, "COIN OF LOD AD 211-217" in Hebrew above and English below. The coin was minted at the beginning of the third century AD by Emperor Caracalla; in the center is the head of Tyche (Fortune) facing left and wearing a crown representing city walls and towers; around is the inscription in Greek, "LUCIA SEPTIMIA SEVERA DIOSPOLIS," the official name of Lod in Roman times.

Edge: Same as M-38.

Number	Date	Metal	Diameter	Weight	Mintage	Issue Price
M-45	1965	Bronze	45mm	40 gm.	15,000	4.00
M-45a	1965	.935 fine silver	45mm	48 gm.	10,000	14.00

Issued December 1, 1965.

JERUSALEM COIN-MEDAL   M-46

Jerusalem is the holy city for all three monotheistic faiths, the spiritual and religious cradle of western civilization. To the people of Israel it is the center of their political life, the capital of their State. A city built on rugged hills with deep valleys between, its landscape is gorgeous, but there are few natural springs and no economic assets. Jerusalem's importance comes from its glorious history. Jerusalem in Hebrew means "city of peace," but its history is turbulent. About three thousand years ago, King David conquered the city and made it his capital. It has been conquered and razed by the Assyrians and the Romans, yet Jerusalem is a living city. All through the ages Jerusalem has been a symbol sacred for millions who have always linked it with the noblest aspirations of mankind. Obverse designed by Jean David, reverse by Alex Berlyne.

OBV: A symbolic and stylized impression of Jerusalem, perched on mountains and crowned by clouds, among which appear the Hebrew inscription "MOUNTAINS ROUND ABOUT JERUSALEM," which is repeated in English in the field.

REV: In the center, a replica of an ancient coin of Jerusalem; on the rim, "BAR-KOCHBA COIN OF JERUSALEM AD 135" in Hebrew above and English below. The coin is a silver "sela" of Bar-Kochba, and presents the four-columned facade of a temple; in the center is an ark for scrolls of the Law, and around is the Hebrew inscription "JERUSALEM."

Edge: Same as M-38; the gold medals have "GOLD 916.6" on the edge.

Number	Date	Metal	Diameter	Weight	Mintage	Issue Price
M-46	1966	Bronze	45mm	40 gm.	15,000	4.00
M-46a	1966	.935 fine silver	45mm	48 gm.	10,000	14.00
M-46b	1966	.9166 fine gold	35mm	29 gm.	3,000	90.00

Bronze and silver medals issued January 1, 1966; gold medals issued February 25, 1966.

ROTHSCHILD MEDAL   M-47

The Rothschild medal was issued in 1966 on the occasion of the inauguration of the Knesset building. Baron Edmond de Rothschild, born in Paris, of the House of Rothschild, became known in Israel as the "Well-Known Benefactor." His undertakings set the foundations for the resettlement of the Jewish people in Israel and were a decisive factor in the restoration of Jewish sovereignty. Born on August 19, 1845, Baron de Rothschild dedicated his work to the traditions of Judaism. Through the Palestine Colonization Association (PICA), formed in 1923, villages sprang up in Judea and Samaria, in Upper and Lower Galilee, swamps were reclaimed, and industry was reactivated. Baron de Rothschild died on November 2, 1935, and was buried in Zikhron, Israel. His son James assumed his father's work, the chairmanship of the PICA. The history of the Rothschilds and PICA is the history of the return to Zion and the re-emergence of a Jewish Commonwealth. James died on May 7, 1947, leaving a letter prepared for Prime Minister David Ben-Gurion ". . . providing for the construction of a new home for the Knesset in Jerusalem. Let the Knesset building become a symbol in the eyes of all men of the permanence of the State of Israel." The dedication of the new home of Israel's legislature is a fitting climax to the House of Rothschild's role in the restoration of Jewish sovereignty in the Promised Land. Designed by master medalist Paul Vincze of London, struck by the Italian State Mint, La Zecca, Rome, Italy.

KNESSET

ROTHSCHILD MEDAL M-47 CONTD.

OBV: In the center, raised cameos with portraits of Baron Edmond de Rothschild, left, and his son James, right; above, the inscription "EDMOND DE ROTHSCHILD FATHER OF THE YISHUV AND HIS SON JAMES WHO GAVE THE KNESSET ITS HOME" in English, below in Hebrew; along the lower rim, the signature of the designer, "P. VINCZE" in English to the left and Hebrew to the right. The signature is in relief lettering.

REV: Three symbolic groups of figures representing the main achievements of the Rothschilds and PICA: two figures gathering grapes representing agriculture and especially viticulture, a mother and her children symbolizing education and child care, and a muscular figure with a wheel emblematic of industry; above all is the Knesset building, placed as a crown symbolizing the achievement of Israel; along the rim on either side of the figure representing industry, the signature of the designer, "P. VINCZE" in English to the left and Hebrew to the right. The signature is incuse.

Edge: Incuse, a miniature emblem of the State and "STATE OF ISRAEL" in Hebrew and English. "SILVER 986" appears on the silver medals, and "GOLD 917" on the gold medals.

Number	Date	Metal	Diameter	Weight	Mintage	Issue Price
M-47	1966	Bronze	59mm	78 gm.	15,000	4.50
M-47a	1966	.986 fine silver	45mm	40 gm.	5,000	14.00
M-47b	1966	.917 fine gold	35mm	30 grn.	3,000	90.00

SINAI CAMPAIGN MEDAL   M-48

The Sinai Campaign medal was issued in 1966 on the occasion of the Tenth Anniversary of the Sinai Campaign on October 29, 1956. For more than two years, terrorists from the Egyptian-occupied Gaza strip and the Peninsula of Sinai had been striking deeply inside of Israel's sovereign territory. At the same time, Egyptian forces blocked ingress to the Gulf of Eilat for Israel shipping and Egyptian guns, set up on the Straits of Tiran, were trained on vessels entering and departing.

The mobilization of Israel's regular army on October 29 and its deployment into the wilderness of Sinai took one hundred hours to reach Sharm el Sheikh at the entrance to the Gulf of Eilat. The achievements of this campaign are three-fold:

The Gaza Strip and the Sinai desert are no longer a springboard for provocation and destructiveness.

The Straits of Tiran leading into the Gulf of Akaba are open once more to international navigation; and Eilat is again the gateway to Israel's sea-lanes to the East.

The lesson of Israel's ability and willingness to defend itself at all times is there for Arab leaders to mark.

Designed by Tsvi Narkis, Tel Aviv. Struck by S. Kretschmer & Sons, Jerusalem.

OBV: In the center, a ship passing through the Straits of Tiran, in stylized form, with a large sun in the background (the two together suggesting tranquility and peace in the Straits); above, the inscription "SINAI CAMPAIGN . TENTH ANNIVERSARY." in English and Hebrew; below, the Proverbs 3, 17, "AND ALL HER PATHS ARE PEACE 1966 (5727)" in Hebrew and English.

REV: In the center, the emblem of the Israel Defence Army, a sword and olive branch; in a stylized form the inscription from the Ecclesiastes 3, 8, in Hebrew "A TIME FOR WAR AND A TIME FOR PEACE"; above around the rim the same verse in English.

Edge: Incuse, a miniature emblem of the State and "STATE OF ISRAEL" in Hebrew and English. "SILVER .935" on the silver medals. All medals are serially numbered.

Number	Date	Metal	Diameter	Weight	Mintage	Issue Price
M-48	1966	Bronze	59mm	100 gm.	15,000	4.50
M-48a	1966	.935 fine silver	45mm	48 gm.	5,000	14.00

THE MINTS

IMPERIAL CHEMICAL INDUSTRIES, Birmingham, England

(ICI in this catalog; also known as the King's Norton Mint and, officially since 1962, the Imperial Metal Industries (Kynoch) Ltd.)
TRADE COINS
- 1949: 1, 5, 10, 25, 50, 100, 250 Pruta
- 1952: 10 Prutot
- 1960: 1 Agora
- 1961: 1, 5, 10 Agorot

ISRAEL GOVERNMENT MINT, Jerusalem, Israel

(The Jerusalem Mint began operations on April 1, 1966, and Trade Coins of 1967 and following years will be struck there.)

ISRAEL GOVERNMENT MINT, Tel-Aviv, Israel

(The Tel-Aviv Mint was closed in October, 1965, after striking all 1966 coins and proof-like sets. Minting operations have been transferred to the new Jerusalem Mint.)
TRADE COINS
- 1948: 25 Mils (Jerusalem private mint)
- 1949: 25 Mils (Jerusalem private mint); and Tel-Aviv.
- 1954: 25, 50, 100 Pruta
- 1955: 100 Pruta
- 1957: 10 Prutot
- 1960: 5, 10, 25 Agorot
- 1961: 5, 10, 25 Agorot
- 1962: 1, 5, 10, 25 Agorot
- 1963: 1, 5, 10, 25 Agorot, ½ and 1 Pound
- 1964: 1, 5, 10 Agorot, ½ Pound
- 1965: 1, 5, 10, 25 Agorot, ½ and 1 Pound
- 1966: 1, 5, 10, 25 Agorot, ½ and 1 Pound

ITALIAN STATE MINT, LA ZECCA, Rome, Italy

FIVE POUND INDEPENDENCE DAY COMMEMORATIVES
- 1963: "Seafaring"
- 1964: "Israel Museum"
- 1965: "Knesset"

STATE COMMEMORATIVE MEDALS
- 1966: Rothschild Medal

S. KRETSCHMER & SONS, Jerusalem, Israel

STATE COMMEMORATIVE MEDALS
Various issues

THE MINT, BIRMINGHAM, LIMITED, Birmingham, England

(MBL in this catalog; also known as Heaton's Mint. Mintmark "H".)
TRADE COINS
- 1949: 1, 5, 10, 25, 50, 100, 250 (cupronickel) Pruta
- 1949: 250, 500 Pruta (silver)

NETHERLANDS STATE MINT, Utrecht, The Netherlands
FIVE POUND INDEPENDENCE DAY COMMEMORATIVES
- 1958: "Menora"
- 1961: "Bar-Mitzvah"
- 1962: "Negev"
- 1966: "Crown of Life"
- 1967: "Eilat"

ONE POUND CHANUKA COMMEMORATIVES
- 1960: "Degania"
- 1960: "Szold"
- 1961: "Heroism and Sacrifice"
- 1963: "18th Century Chanuka Lamp"

HALF-SHEKELS
- 1961
- 1962

TRADE COINS
- 1961: 25 Agorot

THE ROYAL MINT, London, England
BRITISH MANDATORY COINS OF PALESTINE
- 1927: 1, 2, 5, 10, 20, 50, 100 Mils
- 1931: 50, 100 Mils
- 1933: 10, 20, 50, 100 Mils
- 1934: 5, 10, 20, 50, 100 Mils
- 1935: 1, 5, 10, 20, 50, 100 Mils
- 1937: 1, 10 Mils
- 1939: 1, 5, 10, 50, 100 Mils
- 1940: 1, 10, 20, 50, 100 Mils
- 1941: 1, 2, 5, 10, 20 Mils
- 1942: 1, 2, 5, 10, 20, 50, 100 Mils
- 1943: 1, 10 Mils
- 1944: 1, 5, 20 Mils
- 1945: 2 Mils
- 1946: 1, 2, 5, 10 Mils
- 1947: 1, 2, 5, 10 Mils (Never Released)

SWISS FEDERAL MINT, Berne, Switzerland
FIVE POUND INDEPENDENCE DAY COMMEMORATIVES
- 1959: "Ingathering of the Exiles"
- 1960: "Theodor Herzl"

ONE POUND CHANUKA COMMEMORATIVES
- 1958: "Law is Light"
- 1962: "17th Century Chanuka Lamp"

GOLD COINS
- 1960: "Theodor Herzl" 20 Pounds
- 1962: "Chaim Weizmann" 50, 100 Pounds
- 1964: "Bank of Israel" 50 Pounds

TRADE COINS
- 1960: 25 Agorot
- 1961: 5, 10, 25 Agorot
- 1962: 1 Agora
- 1963: 1 Agora, ½ and 1 Pound
- 1964: 1 Agora
- 1965: 1 Agora
- 1966: 1 Agora

BANKNOTE PRINTERS

AMERICAN BANKNOTE COMPANY, New York City, U.S.A.

FIRST ISSUE BANKNOTES: ANGLO-PALESTINE BANK, LTD.
1948: 500 Mils, 1, 5, 10, 50 Palestine Pounds

SECOND ISSUE BANKNOTES: BANK LEUMI LE-ISRAEL B.M.
1952: 500 Pruta, 1, 5, 10, 50 Israel Pounds

ENSCHEDE: Haarlem, The Netherlands

FOURTH ISSUE BANKNOTES: BANK OF ISRAEL
1958: ½, 1 Israel Pound
1960: 50 Israel Pounds

THE ISRAEL GOVERNMENT'S PRINTING PRESS, Jerusalem, Israel

SECOND ISSUE FRACTIONAL NOTES: TREASURY OF ISRAEL
1952: 50, 100 Pruta

THIRD ISSUE FRACTIONAL NOTES: TREASURY OF ISRAEL
1953: 250 Pruta

E. LEVIN-EPSTEIN PRESS, LTD., Israel (for the Government's Printer)

FIRST ISSUE FRACTIONAL NOTES
1948: 50, 100 Mils

THOMAS DE LA RUE & COMPANY, LTD., London, England

PALESTINE CURRENCY BOARD NOTES
1927-1948: 500 Mils, 1, 5, 10, 50, 100 Palestine Pounds

THIRD ISSUE BANKNOTES: BANK OF ISRAEL
1955: 500 Pruta, 1, 5, 10, 50 Israel Pounds

FOURTH ISSUE BANKNOTES: BANK OF ISRAEL
1958: 5, 10 Israel Pounds

ABBREVIATIONS AND SYMBOLS

A	Agora series symbol.
AD	Common era (corresponds to CE as used by the Hebrews).
BC	Before Common Era (corresponds to BCE as used by the Hebrews).
Back	The back side of a banknote. Corresponds to the reverse of a coin.
C	The Commemorative series symbol.
Circ.	Circulated.
DD	Different die.
Face	The front side of a banknote. Corresponds to the obverse of a coin.
G	The Gold coin series symbol.
gm.	Grams.
"H"	The Mint, Birmingham, Ltd. (Heaton's Mint) mintmark.
ICI	The Imperial Chemical Industries, Birmingham, England (until 1962).
L-D	Large Date.
M	The State Commemorative Medal series symbol.
"M"	Special mark found on proof coins since 1959.
MBL	The Mint, Birmingham, Ltd.
M/M	Mintmark.
mm	Millimeters.
N	The Israel Banknote series symbol.
NFS	Not for sale.
NY	The New Years' Remembrance series symbol.
No.	Number
Obv.	Obverse.
P	The Pruta and Mil series symbol.
PCB	The Palestine Currency Board banknote series symbol.
PMC	The Palestine Mandate Coin series symbol.
Rev.	Reverse.
S	The Presentation Set series symbol.
S-D	Small Date.
Unc.	Uncirculated
w/p	With Pearl.
w/o/p	Without Pearl.

BIBLIOGRAPHY

BANK LEUMI LE ISRAEL B.M.
　　1961　Annual Report, Israel
BERUBE, HENRY J.
　　1965　*Israel Coin Market*. Cleveland, Ohio.
BILBY, KENNETH
　　1950　*New Star In The Near East*. New York, Doubleday & Co.
BRENNEMAN, C. G.
　　1954　*A Guide To Bible Study*. San Diego, California.
DIMONT, MAX I.
　　1964　*Jews, God, And History*. New York, New American Library.
EDELMAN, LILY
　　1958　*Israel*. New York, Nelson & Company.
HYMAN, S.
　　1960　*Heroic Israel Today*. New York, G. P. Putnam's Sons.
ISRAEL GOVERNMENT COINS AND MEDALS CORP.
　　1962　*Israel Numismatic Bulletin*. Nos. 1-4, Jerusalem, Israel.
　　1963　*Israel Numismatic Bulletin*. No. 5, Jerusalem, Israel
ISRAEL NUMISMATIC SOCIETY
　　1964　*Israel Numismatic Journal*. Nos. 1-2, Tel-Aviv, Israel.
KADMAN, LEO
　　1959　*Israel's Money*, A Catalogue of the Coins, Medals, and Banknotes
　　　　　Issued 1948-1959. Tel-Aviv, Israel, Israel Numismatic Society
　　　　　Studies and Researches No. III.
　　1963　*Israel's Money*, A Catalogue of the Coins, Commemorative Coins,
　　　　　Medals, and Bank-Notes Issued by the State of Israel, 1948-
　　　　　1963. Tel-Aviv, Israel, Israel Numismatic Society Numis-
　　　　　matic Studies and Researches No. IV.
LEVENSOH, LOTTA
　　1941　*Outline of Zionist History*. New York, Scopus Publishing Co.
MATTHEW, PHILIP J.
　　1965　*Coins of Israel*. Los Angeles, California.
NUROCK, MAX
　　1965　*The Ceremonial Coins and Medals of Israel*. Ariel, A Review of
　　　　　the Arts and Sciences in Israel. Jerusalem, Israel, Cultural
　　　　　Relations Dept., Ministry for Foreign Affairs.
PRIDMORE, FRED
　　1965　*The British Commonwealth of Nations, Part 2, Asian Territories*.
　　　　　London, Spink & Sons Ltd., pp. 13-22.
REIFENBERG, A.
　　1965　*Ancient Jewish Coins*. Fourth Edition, Jerusalem, Rubin Mass.
ROGERS, Rev. E.
　　1914　*A Handy Guide to Jewish Coins*. London, Spink & Sons Ltd.
ROYAL MINT
　　1926　*57th Annual Report of the Deputy Master and Controller of the
　　　　　Royal Mint*. London, pp. 15-16.
WIRGEN, W., and S. MANDEL
　　1958　*The History of Coins and Symbols in Ancient Israel*. New York,
　　　　　Exposition Press Inc.
YEOMAN, RICHARD S.
　　1961　*Moneys of the Bible*. Racine, Wisconsin, Whitman Publishing Co.